THE SPACE AROUND US

A. Edward Tyler

THE
SPACE
AROUND
US

Harper & Row Publishers

NEW YORK, EVANSTON, AND LONDON

For the six J's

Contents

Illustrations

THE SPACE AROUND US

1. The Space Around Us

The Ocean of Space

The space around us is like a sea. The fluid in this sea—the currents, the waves, the tides, are electromagnetic. Since Bohr (or Planck) discovered that energy is matter and matter is energy, we may even think of the planets, and surely of our sun and other stars, as electromagnetic energy, too. In some way that Einstein was only beginning to suspect, electrical fields and magnetic fields, and even gravity, are closely related. Light, too, is only another band of frequencies in the electromagnetic spectrum which makes up the fluid that is space and all that is in it.

As man pushes farther and farther into space with his spaceships, his specialized instruments, and *his mind,* we learn more and more about it.

The more we understand of the universe around us, in spite of its sometimes bewildering and always marvelous variability, the more we discover basic similarities. Oceans of water, oceans of air, oceans of space—all seem characterized by fluids. The fluids of water and air we are familiar with. The fluid of electromagnetic particles, while familiar to the physicist, is something new to most of us. These electromagnetic particles are usually thought of in terms of emanations or radiations which flow from some source to embrace, surround, and engulf other objects. The earth, all the planets for that matter, are continually bathed in the flow of light from our sun—a small star

1

among a hundred billion stars in a small galaxy, one of perhaps a hundred billion such galaxies.

We are accustomed, in this day of nuclear bombs and fallout shelters, to think of radiation as harmful. It isn't harmful in itself —in the case of sunlight it is life-giving. Without the radiation from the sun, which is a vast, *continuing* nuclear fusion, much like millions of hydrogen bombs—without radiation from this sun, our flowering, warm, life-teeming earth would be a barren hunk of rock at the unimaginable cold near absolute zero, whirling forever through complete darkness, in a soundless void.

The ancient philosophers believed all creation to be made up of four elements: earth, air, fire, and water.

The more modern disciplines of chemistry and physics once held that all matter existed in three states: solid, liquid, and gas.

Now that we are learning something of the space around us, we must add a fourth state of matter, called *plasma,* which is the way matter exists in space. Plasma, defined simply, is ionized gas; gas—if you will—made up of charged particles. To understand the stuff of which space is made, let us look briefly at each state of matter.

A solid is characterized by the fact that its component molecules, because of their attraction for each other, are essentially fixed in their positions relative to each other.

A liquid—in which the molecules are still held together by mutual attraction—is a state of matter in which the molecules move more or less freely around and over each other.

In a gas, the molecules are relatively free of each other, being held in the vicinity of the earth by gravity and by the pressure of other molecules above them which are pulled down toward the earth by gravity. In general, the molecules of a gas have energy and are active in trying to escape gravity and other molecules because they have been given energy by the sun, by some artificial means, or because they have been hit by some high-energy particle from outer space.

In a plasma, the molecules themselves are broken up (dissociated). To illustrate what this means, consider the molecules in the air we breathe. The chemists write the symbol for a molecule of oxygen as O_2, nitrogen as N_2, and hydrogen as H_2. When these molecules are present in space (and much hydrogen is present in space) they appear as their constituent ions; thus, H_2 becomes H^+ and H^-. The plus and the minus stand for the electrical charges that ions possess. Near the earth, gravity and pressure from surrounding molecules force most of the H^+ and H^- ions together so they combine into H_2, their electrical charges canceling each other. But out in space the effects of gravity and pressure from other molecules are so small that the natural energy of the H^+ and H^- makes the H_2 molecule break up into its component ions H^+ and H^-. Thus the plasma which makes up the space around us is formed of particles bearing electrical charges as shown by the $+$ and $-$ symbols on the hydrogen ions.

The electrically charged ions are not the only kind of charged particles in space, however. The sources of the plasmas—the nuclear furnaces which we call our sun and the stars—are the producers of such violent bursts of energy that the ions themselves begin to break up. Electrons spin about the atomic nucleus so fast they fly off into space and travel millions of miles as individual, charged electrons. The electrical charge itself may be thousands, millions, or even billions of electron volts. The energy imparted to an atom in the sun (or other star) may be so great that the atomic nucleus itself may fly apart and send a part of the nucleus, called a proton, speeding through space to the farthest planet, or even to a distant galaxy.

Now, let us back up a minute and realize that water (a liquid), air (a gas), and a plasma *are all fluids*. That is, the bits of matter making them up move relatively freely with respect to each other. The gas is more fluid than the liquid and the plasma is more fluid than the gas. Chiefly, this means that movements in these fluids progress more and more rapidly as you go from liquid, to gas, to plasma. But because they are all fluids they have some similar characteristics; there is reason for speaking of the "Ocean of Air" and even of the "Ocean of Space."

The earth has several oceans—the seven seas of fable and fact—which are similar, but each has special characteristics that arise from its location on earth and from the sources of its energy. In a like manner, the universe may be said to comprise myriad oceans. We imagine, from the little we know, that these seas of space have some things in common; but each, like oceans on earth, must have special characteristics, too, dependent on its location in the universe and the sources of its energy. The major source of a space ocean's energy is the star at its center. We believe that each star, like our sun, has its own particular space ocean surrounding it. And each space ocean has characteristics chiefly traceable to the nature of the star that gives it the major portion of its energy.

As with the earth's water oceans, in which waves of various wave lengths are mingled in a tumult of water—ground swell overlaid by storm waves, both cut by chop from a morning off-shore breeze and surface-ruffled by a wayward gust—so in space the all-pervading electromagnetic "fluid" contains at one and the same time the manifestations of gravity, magnetism, light, charged particles, ionization and radiation belts, and plasma jets from the sun. Just as the oceans of the world are each affected by the winds prevailing in their part of the world, so are the oceans of space affected by the energy sources dominant in their part of the universe.

Scientists have recently come to think and speak in terms of the "solar wind" as a force to be reckoned with in the solar system. This solar wind is the pressure of the light emanating from the sun (and of the charged particles, radiating particularly from solar flares) on objects in the vicinity of the sun. At the earth's distance from the sun * these gusty solar winds are enough to force a spacecraft off course on a trip between the earth and Venus, or between the earth and Mars. In the far outer darkness near the planet Pluto the solar winds must be the gentlest of zephyrs, because electromagnetic radiation loses energy at a rate proportional to the square of the distance from the source.

Currents in the oceans of the earth move about at speeds from a fraction of a mile to a few miles per hour. In the ocean of air, currents move generally from a few miles per hour near the earth's surface to several hundred miles per hour in the upper atmosphere. In space,

* Approximately 93,000,000 miles, equaling 1 astronomical unit.

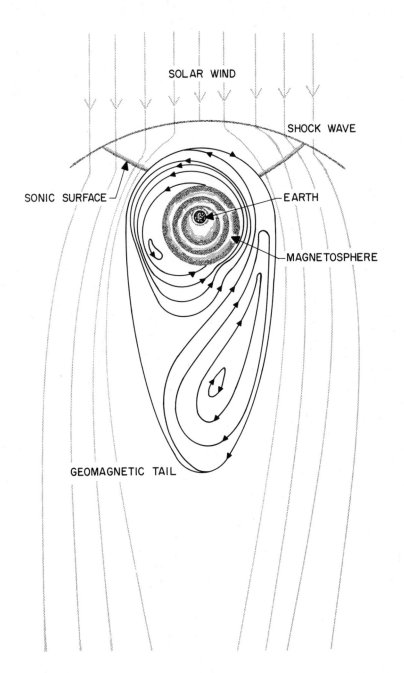

The solar wind flows by the earth, creating a pattern in the magnetic field much like the aerodynamic envelope of a jet plane speeding through the atmosphere.

the currents in the plasma may flow at rates varying from a few hundred miles *per second* to several thousand miles per second. While the difference in speed between ocean currents and plasma currents seems great, the distances (from the Bahamas to Newfoundland, for example, compared with the distance from the sun to earth) are so much greater in space that the speeds may be regarded as more or less proportionate.

Because the charged particles in plasma contain such tremendous amounts of energy, one of the ways of observing them is by the radiation they give off. For example, a particle carrying an electrical charge of about ½ to 5 electron volts produces radio-frequency and infrared radiations. For particles with charges of approximately 5 to 7 electron-volts, the radiations are visible as light. From about 7 to 1,000 electron volts, the radiations are just above the visible, but still in the sunburn spectrum called ultraviolet light. From a little less than 1,000 to about 100 million electron volts, the free electrons and protons produce X-rays, gamma-rays, and the lower-energy cosmic rays. Most of these charged particles emanate from our sun, or at least derive their energy from within the solar system.

Particles, mostly protons, with energies from 1,000,000,000 to 10,000,000,000,000,000,000 (ten quintillion) electron volts are cosmic rays from outside the solar system, originating elsewhere in our galaxy or other galaxies.

These things we have been saying about energies and radiations describe a part of what scientists and engineers call the electromagnetic spectrum. The information in the preceding two paragraphs is presented graphically in the diagram on p. 7.

This information about particle energies is important, because the energy of a given particle can be changed in various ways. Our understanding of the ways in which particles get their energy is, at the present time, the chief basis for theories about whether we live in an expanding universe which was created by one cosmic explosion billions of years ago, or whether our universe operates on some more orderly principle than that of flying debris.

Most of our actual knowledge of space is limited to observations of the solar system; in fact, more correctly, to that part of the solar system circumscribed by the earth's orbit. Most of our beliefs about space beyond the solar system are extrapolations of our solar-system observations or are postulations (educated guesses) of theories which

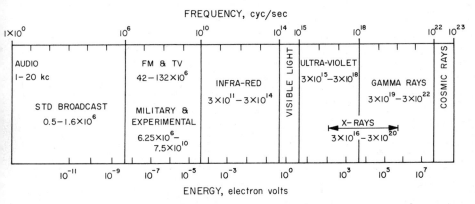

Electromagnetic spectrum, schematic diagram.

seem to fit the fragments of information we get from optical and radio telescopes. These theories are the subject of often bitter debates between scientists and tend to change rather radically over the years as new fragments of information are gained or new theories are proposed which seem to provide a more orderly explanation for known facts.

Einstein, whose genius gave us one of these theories, the theory of relativity (as well as the atom bomb, $E=Mc^2$), at the time of his death was working on a "unified field theory" which was to have harmonized what was known and suspected about electricity, magnetism, and gravity. It is too bad that death cut short his work, because it might have clarified things—particularly with respect to light, magnetism, and gravity—which are still unclear.

We refer to space as an *ocean of energy* because the matter or material of its charged particles is so much less important to our understanding and conquest of space than the electrical charges (energy) carried by the particles.

Palomar photograph of the "Horsehead" nebula showing some of the stuff of interplanetary and interstellar space. (*Mount Wilson and Palomar Observatories*)

Density of matter in interplanetary space seems to average about 20 particles (mostly protons) per cubic centimeter, or about 300 particles per cubic inch. As an idea of how "thin" this spread of matter is, it would take a ball of it the size of the earth to weigh 8 pounds. Actual weight of the earth is about 6 sextillion, 580 quintillion (6,580,000,000,000,000,000,000 or 6.58×10^{21}) tons. Another way of saying it is that the vacuum of interplanetary space is about one million times greater than the best vacuum yet created by man in a laboratory.

Space is an ocean of energy—electrical and magnetic energy. Its currents are electrostatic and magnetic currents; the storms are magnetic storms; the surf is electrostatic surf arising from magnetic storms on the sun; the "solar wind" is a flow of charged particles (electrical energy) emanating from the sun.

Since the sun is so important in this sea of energy which is the space around us, let us briefly consider the sun and its behavior.

The Sun, Our Life-Giving Star

The sun is a vast atomic fusion reaction, equal in power to more than a million 100-megaton hydrogen bombs exploding continuously for probably the last 4 or 5 billion years and perhaps for the next 4 or 5 billion years, too. This tremendous and continuous outpouring of energy from the sun is what makes the earth beautiful and livable for human beings. Only one 200-billionth of the sun's energy reaches the earth, but this provides a continuous 24-hour per day flow of 126 trillion horsepower—about 50,000 horsepower for every man, woman and child now on earth. At this rate, it would require only the horsepower allotted to a family of four to operate the luxury liner *Queen Mary,* if we could just harness 100 per cent of the energy the sun makes available to us.

With this much energy and power available for the catching, it is no wonder that many men and much money are being devoted to studies of ways in which solar power may be made useful on earth. Telephone companies are using "solar cells" which turn light energy into electrical energy—the electrical energy being used to power "booster" stations on long-distance lines. The booster stations strengthen the sound of your voice as it travels over the wires so that it arrives at the ear of the listener as strong as when it left your lips. Spacecraft, too, use solar cells to convert light energy into electrical energy to run the instruments on the spacecraft—enough energy, too, to send radio messages back across millions of miles of space, to tell us what is happening to the spacecraft on its journey through trackless void.

The sun is a very stormy ball of gas which is probably two and one-half times as dense as water near its center; but it is only about one-tenth as dense in the outer layer—the photosphere, which we can see with the naked eye. Temperatures in the sun range from an esti-

A solar prominence 272,000 miles high, the source of some high-energy particles which make up the solar wind. (*Mount Wilson and Palomar Observatories*)

mated 15 million degrees near its center to about 5,000 degrees at the surface of the photosphere.

Outside the photosphere are two more layers: the chromosphere and the corona. The corona is visible to us during an eclipse as a halo of incandescent ionized gas at a temperature of about 1,000,000 degrees near the sun. This corona, less visible as it gets farther from the sun and cooler, is essentially hydrogen gas broken up into protons (the hydrogen nucleus) and free electrons.

The corona appears to be the source of the plasma of charged particles which fills interplanetary space. The charged particles stream out of the sun continuously (in addition to the sun's light) and fill all planetary space out to the earth and beyond, probably at least as far as Saturn. This relatively constant flow at speeds of 200 to 900 miles per second is known as the solar wind.

In addition to the steady output of energy described above, magnetic storms on the sun produce what are called *solar flares,* eruptions of very hot ionized gas which may pour out as much energy in a half hour as one billion H-bombs exploding. The magnetic storms causing these flares are whirling magnetic fields somewhat like the whirling tornadoes that wreak so much havoc on earth. On the surface of the sun, these whirling magnetic vortices seem to suck up some of the sun's flaming surface, give it tremendous energy, and project it out into space at speeds of several thousand miles per second. Protons at these energies have about one-tenth the speed of light.

The Magic of Magnetism

The flow of the solar wind is too strong to be called a breeze, is too subject to change in velocity and intensity to be characterized as anything but gusty. Both the solar wind and the solar storms caused by magnetic disturbances in the sun are channeled to a degree by, and in turn influence the shape of, the magnetic fields which originate in the sun, earth, and some other planets. These magnetic fields, varying greatly in strength from time to time and place to place, seem to permeate all of space that we know anything about.

The causes of strong magnetic fields around the sun, earth, and Jupiter (practically no magnetic field is manifest around Venus), are not completely understood. The rate of rotation seems to be a factor in the strength of a star's or planet's magnetic field. Those which rotate rapidly (as does our earth: one revolution each 24 hours) have a much stronger magnetic field than Venus, for example, which is thought to rotate only once every Venusian year of 225 days.

Another school of thought holds that the presence of a liquid core (such as the molten iron believed to be in the center of the earth) is an important factor in giving a celestial body a strong magnetic field. The effect credited to the molten core may be due, some scientists ·reason, to a speed of rotation in the core different from that in the firm outer covering made up of the mantle and the rocky skin of a planet. In the case of a star such as our sun, the differences in rotation rate would be between the inner, dense gases and the outer, more tenuous layers, which might be slowed by exposure to cosmic radiation and the magnetic fields of other stars or planets.

Another explanation of what produces a magnetic field may be found in the fact that every atom behaves like a small magnet, with a "north" pole and a "south" pole. Particularly in fluid states such as the hot gases making up the stars and in the molten core of the earth, these atoms are free to orient themselves so that most of the "north" poles are pointing "north" and the "south" poles in the opposite direction. In such a tumultuous environment as the sun, or even the molten core of the earth, the atoms are tossed around violently so that they cannot all stay oriented all the time. But, perhaps at any given instant a majority of the atoms are oriented in this manner and so the planet or star has a magnetic field which is the net effect of the little magnetic fields of its countless billions of atoms. By observation we know that the magnetic field of the earth, sun, and other planets is constantly fluctuating, becoming stronger or weaker from moment to moment. Perhaps this fluctuation is a measure of how great a majority of the atoms are properly aligned from moment to moment.

Whatever the explanation for magnetic fields and the related phenomenon of gravity, these things are the glue which holds the universe together (if, indeed, it is being held together at all. There are some who believe that the universe is exploding, with all the galaxies speeding away from each other at millions of miles per hour).

We do know that the earth and other planets are relatively fixed in their orbits about the sun. The force of gravity (balanced by the centrifugal force of their circuits around our·star) is what keeps the orbits of the planets constant. We have learned recently, too, that the magnetic fields of the sun and nearby planets direct to a major degree the solar radiation which fills all solar space with energy and charged particles of one kind or another. Consequently, we can say that, at least in our own back yard, so to speak, magnetism and gravity hold the solar system together in the form that we know it.

Van Allen Belts of Dangerous Radiation

Near the earth the planet's magnetic field *strongly* influences the flow of charged particles; so strongly, in fact, that it traps a great concentration of charged particles in two earth-centered auto-tire-casing–shaped arrangements circling above earth's equator and extending north and south almost to the poles.

The inner radiation zone comprises high-energy protons and is about 2,000 miles above the equator. The outer radiation zone comprises high-energy electrons and is 4,000 to 6,000 miles above the equator. Although these regions of radiation spread toward the earth's north and south poles, they do not quite reach them; consequently, space directly above the north and south poles of earth is free of the dangerous radiation emanating from the Van Allen belts—so called because they were discovered by Dr. Van Allen, of the State University of Iowa, who first devised the necessary experiment and instruments to be carried aloft in 1958 by the United States' first successful space probe (Pioneer IV, launched by the California Institute of Technology's Jet Propulsion Laboratory).

Many scientists are puzzled by the great energy of the charged particles in the Van Allen belts, energy much greater than that of similar particles in the surrounding space. In the diagram on page 7, it is seen that protons with energies of 10^3 electron volts and more are classed as X-rays and gamma-rays, both of which are dangerous to human life. Except for the big bursts accompanying solar flares, most charged particles in space have less energy than this. How does it happen then that the Van Allen belts contain concentrations of charged particles with dangerously higher energies? One explanation may be that the earth's magnetic field holds certain particles in a circular orbit a few thousand miles above the equator, while the earth's motion around the sun swings them through the lines of force of the sun's magnetic field, thus creating an effect similar to that of a cyclotron or synchrotron (atom smasher) on earth which gradually, through repeated electrical impulses, imparts high energies to particles in earthly laboratories.

Without managing to fully understand the earth's Van Allen belts (Saturn seems to have similar bands of radiation), man has nevertheless managed (unintentionally) to modify them. This was done with a high-altitude hydrogen-bomb blast equivalent to 1 million tons of TNT.

The Van Allen belts of dangerous radiation surrounding the earth, a schematic illustration. (*Jet Propulsion Laboratory*)

When asked about possible effects of this blast before it was set off, scientists were most concerned, understandably, about the possibility of "dumping" the natural radiation out of the Van Allen belts onto the earth, where it might endanger humans or animals, and might contaminate food crops. The scientists finally agreed there was little danger of "fallout" from the Van Allen belts, and the high-altitude blast was set off on July 9, 1962. What actually happened as a result was not fallout but the creation of a new belt of man-made radiation in addition to the original Van Allen belts. In the surprise and shock of this unexpected development, scientists and government officials issued conflicting statements, misinterpreted some of the data from instruments sent up into the new radiation belt, and published some alarming comments about increased dangers to manned space travel for the next one hundred years as a result of the blast. Early in 1963, Van Allen claimed that data from several earth satellites bore out his original theoretical predictions that the newly created belt would be essentially dissipated by the summer of 1963.

In March 1963, however, Dr. Van Allen reversed his previous position and conceded that his previous statements about early dissipation of the artificial radiation belt had been based on "intuitive expectations." Irrefutable evidence collected over several months by several earth-orbiting satellites shows that the artificial radiation belt will last for at least a decade. [Note: If the theory of formation of the natural radiation belts suggested earlier is correct, the artificial belt may last much longer, because the particles captured by the magnetic field are "recharged" by the cyclotron effect of the earth's motion through the sun's magnetic field.]

The creation of this artificial radiation belt will make it impossible for a long time to measure the density of protons trapped in the lower, natural Van Allen belt, unless (an outside chance) a giant magnetic storm from the sun washes the artificial belt away.

One amazing fact turned up by the increased observation of the Van Allen belts is that, in response to the pressure of the solar wind, they stream out for 60,000 miles into space like a stretched balloon on the side of the earth away from the sun. The skin of this balloon is an envelope of intense radiation. Inside the balloon, the energy of the particles is below the level that is dangerous to man.

The Wonder of Light

One of the greatest puzzles in the universe is one with which we are all most familiar, and yet no one, not even the scientists, fully understands. This amazing thing is light. Light permeates the entire solar system and all of space. Visible light is a very narrow segment of the electromagnetic spectrum. The spectrum begins with low-frequency radio waves—as low as 500 cycles per second (cps). The radio-wave band is much broader than the band of visible frequencies and goes up to several million cps. Above this we encounter the infrared portion of the spectrum, which can be detected by some photographic film, lead sulphide crystals, a snake's tongue, and your skin—all of which respond to these "heat" rays. Above the infrared, which is *not* visible, we come to visible light, which begins (at a wave length of about .7Å) with *visible red* and goes up one octave through orange, yellow, green, and blue to the *visible violet* (at a wave length of .35 Å). Beyond this is the ultraviolet radiation where a (nonvisible) photon of light has an energy of about 1 electron volt (see p. 7). One of the mysteries of light is that it seems to best illustrate the interchangeability of energy and matter (or mass, as the scientists refer to it). Light, in most instances, does not seem to consist of charged particles —it acts essentially like the *energy* on a charged particle, without the particle. Yet light has enough mass (weight, if you wish) that when it falls upon a light motor in a jeweler's window—one of those little paddle wheels in a vacuum bulb, with one side of each paddle painted black and the other side silver—it spins the little wheel at high speed. Light also has enough mass that, in the boundless reaches of space, it can push a spacecraft off course. Light seems to be pulses of energy (photons) which, as they go forward at 186,000 miles per second, are accompanied by, or urged on their way by magnetic waves which move at right angles to the direction in which the light is traveling. When light strikes the earth, or a spacecraft in space, or a molecule in our atmosphere, the light energy is turned partly into heat energy.

That part of the light that is *not* converted into heat when it strikes something is reflected or (if the object is transparent) transmitted. On earth, much sunlight is reflected back and forth between droplets of moisture and motes of dust in our atmosphere. The size of these objects, particularly the moisture droplets, is such that the blue wave lengths of light are most reflected. Thus we have a blue sky—because we see the blue portion of the sun's light reflected back and forth in the upper atmosphere. Large dust motes in the lower atmosphere, or smoke from forest fires, produce spectacular red sunsets, because these particles are big enough to reflect the longer, red wave lengths. In space, where there is no moisture and not enough dust to reflect the light, the sky is a deep black in which the stars and planets shine with an unwinking persistence.

One of the most spectacular lights seen on earth is the northern lights, or aurora borealis, which appears over the North Pole and sometimes extends down over the temperate zone. The same phenomenon occurring over the South Pole is called the aurora australis. These displays are caused by the high-energy particles released by a solar flare striking the ionized air of our upper atmosphere. To the ions, themselves, is transferred so much energy from these impacts that they glow like the ionized gas in a neon or fluorescent tube. The aurorae have the appearance of rays (following the lines of the earth's magnetic field) or bands of red, yellow, green, and blue. Sometimes they appear as great curtains of light suspended in the heavens, swaying, forming, and reforming in the ever-changing and shifting magnetic field that surrounds and protects the earth.

2. Travelers in Space

The ocean of space that surrounds us—empty as it seems, except for the space fluid of energy—actually is traveled by quite a few voyagers. Some of the ships in this sea of energy are natural—put there by the Creator and the processes which He has set in motion. These are the planets and their satellites, plus asteroids that follow quite regular routes in the solar system. Still within the solar system are more exotic and less predictable visitors—comets and meteors.

In recent years, since the launching of the first Sputnik by the Russians in 1957, a considerable host of man-made craft have begun to travel in space, too.

The man-made spacecraft, like the natural, fall into several well-defined classes. First are the near-earth space probes, such as high-altitude rockets, which go up from the surface of the earth for a few score or even a few thousand miles, only to return to the surface immediately.

There are also satellites which are put into orbits about the earth. These orbits may be essentially circular or highly elliptical (eccentric). Such satellites may orbit the earth a few times or may be launched on voyages lasting months, years, or even thousands of years (Explorer I). Man probably soon will launch satellites to orbit other planets, but as this is written none has been successfully put into an orbit around any planet other than earth.

There are also space probes which escape the cage of the earth's gravity to travel in interplanetary space, but these cannot yet escape the inexorable demands of the sun. The most far-ranging "space" probes launched to date have ended as satellites (man-made miniature planets, if you wish) of the sun—orbiting it in an elliptical path forever and ever.

The fourth class of man-made space travelers is space debris— burned-out rocket casings, fragments of boosters which have lifted spacecraft into orbit or trajectory and which have inescapably followed the craft they once served.

Natural Travelers

Let us look briefly at the wonderful and varied *natural* travelers in this ocean of space first. And let us start with the planets.

The Lively Family of Planets

Our star, the sun, as we all know, is a part of the galaxy or star island that we call the Milky Way. The sun is about three-fifths of the way out from the center of this dish-shaped collection of probably 100 billion other stars, most of which are larger than our sun. This gigantic star island is revolving at speeds which are fantastic by comparison with anything that we know on earth, but the galaxy is so huge that it takes it 200 million years to revolve just once. As the sun revolves with the galaxy, maintaining its place in relation to the other stars in the galaxy, it takes along with it its family of nine planets. The planets are an interesting and varied lot, and some of their characteristics are given in Table 1.

The planet closest to the sun is Mercury, and its average distance from the sun is 35.5 million miles which in solar distances is very small. Mercury has an elliptical orbit: it comes as close as 28 million miles and gets as far away as 43 million miles from the sun. The planet farthest out that we know anything about now is Pluto, which also has an elliptical orbit such that it approaches within 2 billion, 700 million miles of the sun at its nearest approach, or perihelion, and retreats as far as 4.6 billion miles away from the sun at aphelion. This elliptical orbit of Pluto's creates somewhat of a solar traffic

The great nebula in Andromeda, a galaxy somewhat similar to our own Milky Way, if we could see it from the same vantage point from which this photograph was taken. (*Mount Wilson and Palomar Observatories*)

problem because, at its nearest approach, it is closer to the sun than its nearest neighbor, Neptune, whose average distance from the sun is 2 billion, 796 million, 600,000 miles. This is somewhat like changing from lane to lane in a freeway without signaling.

Mars is another planet with a highly elliptical orbit, and is farther from the sun than is the earth. It comes as close as 128.5 million miles to the sun and gets as far away as 154.5 million miles. The earth, of course, averages 93 million miles from the sun in a relatively circular orbit, and because a mile is such a small measure to use in figuring astronomical distances, scientists have now come to use the earth's distance from the sun as the "astronomical unit" (AU), measuring distances to other planets and other parts of the solar system in astronomical units instead of miles. Of course, beyond the solar system, the standard unit of measurement is the light year, which is the distance that light can travel at 186,000 miles per second in a year, approximately 6 trillion miles. The nearest star, Alpha Centauri, is approximately four and a half light years away.

The nine planets, in the order of their distance from the sun, are: Mercury, Venus, earth, Mars, Jupiter, Saturn, Uranus, Neptune, and Pluto. Of these, Mercury and Venus have no moons at all (Pluto is so far away we can't tell for sure whether it has moons or not). All the rest have moons. The earth has one moon, which is about 250,000 miles away and which has a "retrograde" rotation (so-called because it turns opposite to the direction of the moon's orbit around the earth). This keeps the same face of the moon toward the earth at all times, since its rotation rate and its rate of revolution around the earth are identical—twenty-eight days. Mars has two moons, but they are much closer to Mars than the earth moon is to the earth. Mars's farthest moon is 12,500 miles from its surface and its nearest moon is only 3,700 miles from its surface. Jupiter has twelve moons, of which eight revolve around the planet in a west-to-east direction, and four in an east-to-west direction—another traffic problem. Saturn, which has two rings of debris left over apparently from broken-up moons, still has nine moons intact and orbiting it in a normal manner from west to east. The closest one is 760,000 miles from the planet and the farthest, 2.2 million miles from the planet. Uranus has five moons, all of which revolve around it not only from east to west (which is counter to the normal direction in the solar system), but also in a plane which is perpendicular to its axis of rotation. This, however, is Uranus' fault, because Uranus points its axis of rotation at the sun and in effect rolls around the sun on its side, while the moons revolve about Uranus in the plane of Uranus' orbit around the sun, called the ecliptic. Neptune seems to have only two moons, one of which revolves around it in the normal west-to-east direction; the other in the east-to-west direction.

The planets come in all sizes, too. The earth and Venus are almost twins, with 7,900 miles and 7,700 miles for their respective diameters. Mercury and Mars are the pygmies of the solar system with only 3,100 and 4,200 miles for their diameters. Jupiter is the biggest planet in the solar system, with a diameter of 86,000 miles, followed by Saturn, whose diameter is 73,000 miles. Uranus, the side-rolling planet, is 32,000 miles in diameter and Neptune is 27,700 miles in diameter. Pluto, the farthest of all from the sun, probably has a diameter of about 3,600 miles though it is so far away it has proved difficult to measure this with any accuracy.

Planets are heavy and light, also. The earth, and possibly Pluto, are the two densest planets in the solar system. Venus has a density approximately 95 per cent that of the earth, while Mercury's density is 67 per cent that of the earth. Some of the bigger ones are pretty lightweight stuff, with Jupiter and Uranus being only 25 per cent of the density of the earth and Saturn only 12 per cent as dense as the earth. The stuff of Saturn is so light that it would float on water, if there were any water there to float it on, but Saturn's atmosphere seems made mostly of methane and ammonia (probably frozen) with no water vapor or water in evidence. The densities of Mars and Neptune are 0.70 and 0.29, respectively.

As you will suspect, the closer the planet is to the sun the hotter it is, and the farther from the sun the colder it is. Mercury seems to have a surface temperature of about 770°. Venus, because of the greenhouse effect achieved by a smog-like cloud cover and the heavy concentration of CO_2 in its lower atmosphere, has a surface temperature of around 800°. The surface of both these planets is hot enough to melt many metals, including lead, tin, potassium, cadmium, sodium, lithium, and others. The earth's temperature you know about, and beyond the earth comes Mars which, because of its thin atmosphere, probably warms up to a comfortable 70° to 100°F. in the daytime, but, also because of its thin atmosphere, probably drops off to an uncomfortable 150°F. below zero at night. Mars's distance from the sun is only about 60 per cent greater than that of the earth from the sun. The next planet beyond Mars is Jupiter, which is more than five times as far from the sun as is the earth. As you may suspect, Jupiter's temperature, or at least the temperature of the clouds of gas which swirl continually about it, is a cold 225°F. below zero. Saturn's temperature is estimated at 250° F. below zero, Uranus and Neptune at 300° F. below zero; Pluto probably approaches absolute zero at about 400° F. below zero.

All the planets are held in their orbits around the sun by the force of gravity—that is, the attraction between the planet and the sun. This attraction is somewhat like magnetism and, as you know from experiments with home magnets, the farther apart two magnets are the less strong their attraction for each other. In the solar system the force of gravity attracts the planets to the sun, while their centrifugal force, the speed with which they revolve around the sun, tends to pull them away until the two forces are exactly balanced. For this reason, the farther from the sun you get, the slower the orbital speed of the planets. Mercury travels around the sun at a fast 30 miles per second, Venus at about 20 miles per second, and the earth only slightly slower at 19 miles per second. Mars has an orbital speed of 15 miles per second, and Jupiter drops to 8, and Saturn to 6; Uranus, twice as far from the sun as Saturn, has an orbital speed of 4.6 miles per second. Neptune and Pluto are the slowpokes of the solar system, with speeds of 3.5 and 3.0 miles per second, respectively.

In the space between Mars and Jupiter are some small planets or asteroids which some think resulted from the breakup of a full-scale planet with an orbit in this area. Up to the present, almost 1,600 asteroids have been identified and their orbits determined. Although new asteroids are discovered each year, they are usually smaller than those previously identified, which indicates that the largest asteroids have probably all been found. The largest one is Ceres, which is about 500 miles in diameter. The smallest one named is a chunk of rock called Eros; it is about 15 miles long and one mile in diameter.

The sun and its family of planets could well be compared with a small and rather simple atom, in which the sun is the nucleus and the planets are the electrons, cruising in orbits about the central nucleus. And there are probably two significant differences. One is the fact that the space between the sun and the planets is not nearly as great in proportion to their size as is the space between the nucleus and the electrons in an atom. In other words, the solid matter of this book you hold in your hand, made up mainly of atoms of carbon, hydrogen, and oxygen, has less material in it, relatively, than the solar system, in which it is almost 5 billion miles from the sun out to the farthest planet, Pluto. The other significant difference is that, while the orbits of the planets are not all in the same plane about the sun, the planes are fairly close to each other, making an angle of not more than 24° from the one tilted the farthest one way to the one tilted the farthest the other way. It is believed that in atoms the plane of the orbits of electrons are much more divergent, reaching a maximum at which one orbit is perpendicular to, or 90° from, another.

Although not a lot is known about the magnetic fields of other planets and their moons, there are a few bits of knowledge even in this difficult area. Venus, particularly since the voyage of the spacecraft, Mariner II, is known to have no measurable magnetic field on its sunlit side out as far as the 21,600 miles which was the closest approach of Mariner. This measurement, or lack of it, seems in agreement with at least two of the three major theories about magnetic fields of planets.

The pressure of the solar wind against the sunlit side of a planet pushes its magnetic field (if any) closer to the planet on that side than it does on the dark side, where that same solar wind seems to draw out the magnetic field to sometimes great distances. For example, on the sunlit side of the earth we have a measurable magnetic field out to about 40,000 miles; on the side of the earth away from the sun this magnetic field extends out in a balloon-like envelope for at least 60,000 miles. The main strength of the magnetic lines of force seems to be in the surface of this envelope (wherein are trapped also the high-energy particles of the Van Allen belts), with reduced magnetic force inside the envelope and almost no high-energy particles. Thus, with Venus closer to the sun than the earth, the force of the solar wind on the sunlit side of the planet could be expected to press its magnetic field closer to the planet than the earth's magnetic field is pressed to the earth.

The second theory about magnetic fields is that the faster a planet's rotation the more strength its magnetic field is likely to have. As recent investigations have shown (both the Mariner II mission and the Venus radar experiments of Caltech's Jet Propulsion Laboratory) Venus seems to rotate hardly at all and, in fact, may continually present the same side toward the sun. Presumably, this would result in almost no magnetic field for Venus.

The third theory concerning magnetic fields has to do with their development as a result of a "dynamo effect" in the molten core of the planet. Determination of whether or not Venus has a molten core will have to await our landing some instruments there to measure "Venus quakes" and radio the information back to earth. From these radioed data we may be able to deduce whether or not the planet has a molten core.

However, there is at least one other planet that we know has a strong magnetic field, and this is the planet of Jupiter, which is ten times larger and rotates twice as fast as the earth.

All in all, the planets make up a lively and interesting group of travelers in this sea of space, and we shall be eager to learn more about them through some of the space ships and other tools of discovery that man is learning to use in study of our solar system.

Some of the planets' moons may also have magnetic fields. For example, Russian investigators report that our own moon, on its sunny side, has a magnetic field $\frac{1}{3}$ of 1 per cent of the earth's magnetic field at the equator. This very low value is believed to be chiefly accounted for by the fact of the moon's very slow rotation rate: it turns on its axis only once in every revolution about the earth, once in twenty-eight days. But some of the other planets, more bountifully endowed with moons than ours, may have some which rotate rapidly enough to create strong magnetic fields of their own. The interaction of planetary and lunar magnetic fields near these planets should trap charged particles from the sun and from outer space in vivid night-time displays of color which should surpass anything seen in earth's aurorae.

Meteors

Other natural travelers in this sea of space are the meteors and meteorites. Some of these are big enough to survive the fiery plunge through the earth's atmosphere and blast tremendous holes in the earth's surface, as at Meteor Crater in Arizona.

A few years ago a woman in Kansas was struck on the hip by a meteor about twice as large as her fist, which had penetrated the roof and the ceiling of her living room to give her a bruising blow as she rested on a davenport.

The most common meteors or meteorites are often seen on a summer evening as shooting stars. These leave a bright trail in the sky long enough to intrigue the youngsters or signify something important to lovers, but burn out before they reach the surface of the earth.

Early experiments with spacecraft and satellites showed that in the vicinity of the earth there was a host of micrometeorites, ranging from the size of a grain of sand down to mere specks of dust with a mass of no more than one-trillionth of a pound. Micrometeorite counters sent aloft on early sounding rockets and on earth satellites often counted as many as three of these an hour, striking a plate about six inches square. Considering the extreme vacuum of interplanetary space this is a very thick concentration of micrometeorites. But with the excursion of Mariner II to Venus it was discovered that, once beyond the earth's magnetic field, the micrometeorite population dropped off to almost nothing. In the more than one hundred days it took for the cruise to Venus, the micrometeorite counter aboard Mariner II counted only three micrometeorites beyond the immediate vicinity of the earth.

Scientists have theorized that the presence of the thick micrometeorite dust near the earth is material left over from the earth's formation; or, conversely, that this "stardust" may be left over from the breakup of an earlier earth moon or a collision of asteroids in the vicinity of the earth. Still another postulation might be that, as matter flows out from the sun in the form of charged particles, these particles are crowded closer together by the necessity of detouring around the earth's magnetic field, and by the chance of this closer contact, particles of opposite charges that have suitable chemical affinities combine to form micrometeorites.

The Mystery of Comets

Comets are perhaps the most interesting natural travelers in this ocean of space that surrounds us. This may be partly due to the fact that we know so little about them: A mystery is always intriguing!

Comets are also the special preserve of the amateur astronomer. Far distant galaxies can only be examined with multimillion dollar observatories supported by universities or research foundations. But almost any amateur with a home-made telescope and perhaps even a hand-ground lens, can look for comets within our solar system. In fact, many amateurs do. All comet discoveries are, by general agreement, telegraphed to the Harvard Observatory, which is the clearinghouse for this type of astronomical information. If you are first in discovering a comet, you can have it named after you. As long as men study the heavens (they have been doing so since the beginning of recorded history and will probably do so increasingly in the future) your name will be attached to this comet. This is an interesting form of immortality.

Comets are generally considered to be creatures of the solar system, controlled by the sun's attraction, in great elliptical orbits of which one focus is the sun and the other a point in space as much as several billion miles from the sun. Because of their very long paths, some comets have a period (the time it requires for them to complete their orbit around the sun) of a thousand years or more.

Comets can be disturbed in their natural, or original, orbits, however, by coming close to the planets in the solar system. Jupiter seems to be the chief offender in this regard, and many comets coming close to Jupiter have had their orbits so shortened by the attraction of Jupiter that their period of orbiting has been much reduced from what it once was. In fact, there are about thirty-four comets which have had this experience over the past eons so that their orbits no longer extend much beyond Jupiter and their periods of orbit have been shortened from unknown hundreds or even thousands of years to a relatively few years. In fact, the comet having the shortest known period, 3.3 years, and called Encke, is one of these. The comets which have had their orbits and their periods reduced by Jupiter have come to be known as Jupiter's comet family.

The reason that Jupiter is so influential on comet orbits is its great size, high rotation rate, and consequent strong magnetic field.

Sometimes, however, the effect of Jupiter on a comet's orbit is just the opposite. When a comet approaches Jupiter in such a manner that the influence of the planet's gravitation lengthens the comet's orbit, the shape of the orbit may change from an ellipse to a parabola, which, as you know, has an open end. Thus, the comet departs the solar system and goes on into interstellar space, never to return to the influence of the sun. It is conceivable, of course, that this comet may cross the gravitational pull of another star and become, in this way, a comet in a great elliptical orbit around another sun.

Speculations about what comets are have been quite wide-ranging. The fact that comets travel very rapidly in relation to the position of the earth has made it difficult to observe them carefully. Observations with optical telescopes have not been too satisfactory in any event because of the optical peculiarities of comets. As observed through an optical telescope, a comet appears to be composed of a central nucleus of great brilliance surrounded by a head or coma of one or more layers and, in most cases, accompanied by a tail. The nucleus has been observed to have a diameter as great as 8,000 miles (approximately the diameter of earth), while comet heads sometimes extend to a diameter of 100,000 miles. The tail accompanying the comet may be as much as 100 million miles in length and 1 million miles in diameter, although there are some comets which appear to have no tails.

We say that the comet is "accompanied" by its tail, rather than say it is followed by the tail. This is because the tail does not always follow the comet. As the comet goes around the sun, the tail points away from the sun so that, as the comet recedes from the sun, the tail actually precedes the comet.

An interesting thing about comet tails is that they seem to be almost optically transparent. Even a very faint star can be seen through a million miles of comet tail. We know that we cannot see faint stars when they are near the horizon of the earth because the earth's atmosphere absorbs their light. Consequently it appears that perhaps ten miles of air near the earth's surface absorbs more light than a million miles of comet tail.

Comets also have other interesting characteristics. While some appear to show little change except for the direction of the tail and the increasing length of the tail as they approach the sun, like Halley's comet, other comets change drastically in appearance even from day to day. Morehouse's comet, appearing in 1908, showed marked changes from one night to the next. On the night of September 30, for example, it had a broad, fairly short tail extending outward at about 80° from the line of the comet's travel; beyond this for a considerable distance, twenty-five or thirty times the diameter of the comet's head, extended a more tenuous tail. On the night of October 1, the main tail of the comet seemed to have separated from the head by perhaps ten diameters and to be attached by only two thin filaments with the tail itself dissipating broadly in the distance. On the night of October 2, the former tail was just a thin cloud at a distance of perhaps 30 diameters from the head, while the comet itself had extended rays of light over an angle of about 45° perpendicular to its direction of travel, the longest ray extending out ten or twelve diameters from the head.

A photograph of the comet, Cunningham, December 24, 1940, showing stars (straight lines made because the earth rotated during an exposure which was kept fixed on the comet). The stars clearly visible through the comet's tail. (*Mount Wilson and Palomar Observatories*)

Astronomers have long tried to explain the construction of comets on the basis of a nucleus containing some kind of solid matter. However, they run into the difficulty that most simple solids of which humans know would hold together better than some comet nuclei seem to do. For example, in some comets the nucleus appears to be broken up by the difference in the sun's attraction on the near and far sides—or perhaps some pressure of the solar wind. Small solids under these conditions would have sufficient cohesion to resist this breakup; large solids would have enough gravitational stability to resist it. Also, comets have been observed to go through the satellite system of Jupiter—that comet-orbit–changing planet—without affecting the motion of Jupiter's own satellites by any amount that could be measured from earth. For these reasons scientists are puzzled, for certainly a mass the size of observed comet nuclei would affect the orbits of the satellites of Jupiter in passing.

Despite these unresolved problems, astronomers have in the past described comet nuclei as consisting of a mass of small particles, perhaps spaced yards apart, but held together loosely by their mutual attraction.

Other astronomers believe that comets are formed in cold outer space from dust particles believed to exist there and combined with icy particles of methane, ammonia, and water. This group holds that the "ices" may form as much as 70 per cent of the mass of the comet —the other 30 per cent being formed from interstellar dust and rocky and metallic materials such as are found in meteorites. According to this theory, as the comet approaches the sun, the heat of the sun melts away the ice, releasing the meteorite particles into space to form the tail of the comet. If these particles are small enough, the pressure of the sun's light, or the solar wind, would have a greater effect on these particles than the attraction of solar gravity.

In the light of the discovery by the Mariner mission to Venus that micrometeorite particles in interplanetary space are much less numerous (perhaps by a factor of 10,000 to 1) than had been expected, and by virtue of a new look at some of the other phenomena of comets, it may be that a new theory is in order.

This observer would like to suggest that comets do not have mass in the ordinary sense, but are, rather, intense local magnetic fields somewhat (in a smaller way) like the magnetic vortexes observed on the surface of the sun, or like whirlpools in water where two currents join. In the overlapping magnetic fields which exist in space, originating in the sun, in the planets, and in some of the planet satellites or moons, these vortexes develop in much the same manner as whirlpools develop at the borders between impinging currents of water at a confluence of rivers. In the sea of energy which is space, the pressures are relatively low, by earthly standards, and relatively constant. Under these conditions, a local magnetic field could orbit the sun much as comets do. The light which a comet appears to emit could be the luminescence engendered by the encounter of this local magnetic field with the charged particles in the solar wind. This would also account for the fact that the comet's tail always points away from from the sun. The kind of light we are seeing would be similar to that observed near earth when a magnetic storm on the sun increases the intensity of the solar wind until its action in the magnetic field of the earth creates the aurora borealis, or aurora australis. This theory would also explain why a comet can pass near the orbit of Jupiter without affecting the orbits of Jupiter's satellites; equally it would explain why comets coming near to Jupiter—which has an extremely strong magnetic field—would have their orbits so distorted as to substantially reduce their period of travel or to send them out into space never to return. The effect of a strong magnetic field like that surrounding Jupiter would be great on a little "magnetic whirlwind" which appears to us as a comet. Equally, this theory could explain why comet nuclei break up (into two smaller local magnetic fields under the pressure of a magnetic burst from the sun); or how a comet's tail might drift away from the comet—the luminescence occasioned by the interaction of a magnetic field and charged particles could leave the charged particles still glowing for some time after the magnetic field (the nucleus of the comet) had passed by.

Whatever we may now think of comets or whatever our future research proves to be the facts about them, they remain the most exotic and exciting of the natural travelers in the sea of space which surrounds us.

Man-Made Travelers

Most people assume that the space age began on October 4, 1957, when the Russians launched a 184-pound earth satellite called Sputnik I. This is really not true.

You might say the space age began with the Chinese, who used rockets in warfare, or the Turks, who did the same thing several thousand years ago. Rockets were more recently used in the war of the American Revolution, and this fact is commemorated by the line in our national anthem, which reads, "By the rocket's red glare." In the twentieth century, the earliest proponent of rocket propulsion was a man by the name of Goddard, an American; he preceded Wernher von Braun and other Germans of the Pennemünde rocket installation during World War II by about two decades. The German V-2 rockets were undoubtedly the forerunners of modern space vehicles, and the V-2s were designed to rise to an altitude of 200 or 250 miles before plunging their destructive warheads on London.

The Space Race: United States vs. Russia

After the war, the United States brought a number of German rocket experts, including Dr. Wernher von Braun, to this country to help improve our military technology with this kind of weapons.

California's Jet Propulsion Laboratory (JPL), however, had done much research on rocketry even before the war. Its most useful wartime product (one which helped establish what is now the Aerojet General Division of General Tire and Rubber Company) was a rocket "bottle" which could be fastened under the wings of heavily loaded airplanes on short runways for jet-assisted takeoff (JATO). JPL had also been developing, for the ordnance department of the Army, a rocket called the Corporal.

With captured bits of German V-2s, the know-how of Wernher von Braun and his associates, and with the Corporal rocket mounted piggyback on a V-2, some altitude records were established as early as 1947, ten years before the Russians launched the Sputnik.

If you wonder why rockets are so important in a discussion of the space age, it is simply that rockets do not have to breathe air in order to function properly. All other propulsion systems in general use need to breathe air to accomplish combustion of the fuel to produce energy to accomplish the work they are designed for. Rockets, however, carry both the fuel they need plus the oxygen necessary to oxidize or "burn" it, and thus release its energy. Because of this simple fact, rockets can go beyond the earth's atmosphere and do work in space. For this reason, the space age depends upon the techniques of rocketry for its present and near-future successes.

The Russians did not talk much about what turned out to be their space program before they launched Sputnik I on October 4, 1957, so we do not know what their plans were.

The United States, however, announced that it hoped to launch a space vehicle which would become a satellite of the earth during the International Geophysical Year (I.G.Y.). It was hoped that this satellite, to be named Vanguard I, would orbit the earth at altitudes of 300 to 700 miles and might be able to determine more exactly (1) the shape of the earth, (2) the exact location of things on the earth, and (3) something about the space near the earth, particularly information on the earth's magnetic field and whether or not there was harmful radiation outside the earth's atmosphere.

The I.G.Y. was actually an eighteen-month period extending from July 1, 1957, through December 1958.

When the Russians surprised the world by launching Sputnik I in October of 1957—and when they surprised themselves as well as the world by having achieved such a "public relations" coup—the United States made every effort to speed the launching of the Vanguard I.

Luck was not with us, however, and the first attempt to launch Vanguard I on December 6, 1957, ended in a failure because the first stage of the rocket booster lost its thrust two seconds after launch and the entire vehicle was consumed in flames over the Atlantic.

Shortly after Russia launched the Sputnik I, Dr. William Pickering, director of the JPL, was in Washington pressing for action on a program he had been recommending for some time. The program was simply to utilize the Juno missile then being developed by the

Army's Redstone Arsenal (under the guidance of Wernher von Braun) as a booster to put into space a pencil-shaped satellite called Explorer I, which would carry out some of the same scientific experiments which had originally been planned for a later Vanguard. Dr. Pickering got approval, and in the eighty days between November 9, 1957, and January 31, 1958, Dr. Pickering and his organization matched Explorer I to its booster and launched the spacecraft into a 224/1,584-mile orbit, using a four-stage Jupiter C rocket. The pencil-shaped spacecraft (including its final rocket stage) weighed 30.8 pounds and carried cosmic-ray and micrometeorite measuring devices. Explorer I's discovery of the Van Allen radiation belts has been regarded as the most significant discovery of the International Geophysical Year. Valuable information was also gained about micrometeorites near the earth's surface. Explorer I kept sending back information about its travels until May 23, 1958, at which time its batteries gave out; but, as this is written, it continues to circle the earth as the oldest man-made satellite still in orbit.

Recognizing that the discovery of the Van Allen belts by Explorer I was the most important event of the I.G.Y., which also witnessed the launching of Sputnik I, it seems appropriate to ask why the Russians are so far ahead of us in space.

The simple answer is that they are not!

The Russians have, however, been much more successful than the United States in the propaganda battle for credit in space accomplishments.

Part of the success of the Russian propaganda had to do with the fact that their accomplishment burst upon the world with no previous announcement and thereby achieved an effect of tremendous surprise. In the advertising business this is called "impact." The impact was even greater because Russia, at that time, was still regarded as being somewhat backward technically; but the Russians had invaded Germany, too, and they had taken their share of German rocket experts back to Russia. The Russians had said nothing about their efforts in this field until they were ready to present mankind with a *fait accompli.*

A simple comparison of the space achievements of the two countries shows that the United States is far ahead of Russia in all space activities except the single fact of the capability to lift a large pay load at a single launching.

Even this achievement of Russia stems from lack of capability in another very important area, that of miniaturizing electronic and electromechanical components necessary to go into spacecraft and, incidentally, into atom bombs.

In fact, had it not been for American progress in making more efficient (and less bulky) atom bombs, we would have needed to build as big rockets as Russia did and therefore could have lifted as big payloads into orbit as they.

The April 20, 1963, issue of the *Saturday Evening Post* gives an interesting sidelight on this matter (page 18). The event described took place in 1953 in San Diego, California, in the room occupied by the Board of Directors of Convair, then a division of Consolidated Vultee Aircraft Corporation. A Committee, headed by the late Dr. John von Neumann, Caltech professor and research Fellow, was studying missile development and questioning company officials on their proposal to build an ICBM called the Atlas to meet United States military requirements. When the Convair engineers mentioned the weight of the warhead they had been told to plan for, Dr. von Naumann was puzzled; he realized that Convair was planning for a far heavier pay load than was necessary in the light of the then-current developments of the atom and hydrogen bombs. Under strict security rules he was not authorized to say so. After the conference, von Naumann had a member of his committee draw aside a Convair vice-president, Thomas G. Lanphier, Jr., and suggest that Lanphier visit him in Washington as soon as possible. Upon Lanphier's arrival in Washington, he was told, "You can't tell your people why or who told you, but let me tell you that the payload for that missile is going to be much smaller than you think. Instead of the __ pounds you're planning for, it's going to be __ pounds."

The Convair vice-president was stunned! The change in weight was so great that instead of the five-engine missile they had been expecting to develop they would need only a three-engine missile, which meant incalculable savings in both time and money. This was

The assembly line at Astronautics Division, General Dynamics, San Diego, where Atlas missiles are made for both military and space uses. (*General Dynamics/ Astronautics Division*)

early in 1953, four and a half years before Sputnik was launched—plenty of time for us to have built a big rocket if we had needed one for our improved nuclear bombs.

The boosters that are carrying spacecraft into space today were not intended to carry spacecraft at all—they are simply military missiles which have been adapted to use in the space race. Russia had to build a big missile because it had a clumsy bomb; the United States did not need to build a big missile because it had a much improved bomb: the same tremendous explosive power but not nearly so much tonnage. Very shortly, in the United States at least, spacecraft will be carried aloft by boosters intended specifically for this purpose and only secondarily useful for military purposes. But early boosters, both in Russia and the United States, were originally designed for military purposes and only adapted for use in launching space vehicles. Consequently Russia at first could boost more tonnage into space with a single launch than we could, for the apparently contradictory reason that both our military and space technologies are ahead of theirs. The weight-lifting championship went to the United States on January 29, 1964, with the launching of Saturn SA-5, which carried aloft a payload of 37,500 pounds, doubling the best Russian effort to that date.

To see how the space race really stands, look at Table 2. This table, prepared by TRW Space Technology Laboratories, Inc., Los Angeles, shows all spacecraft launched from the launching of Sputnik in October 1957 to the present writing.

To summarize the United States performance and compare it with Russian performance, the following data are of interest: In this period 176 United States spacecraft have been put into earth orbit in comparison with 43 Russian spacecraft put in earth orbit. The United States has had two spacecraft impact on the moon, while the Russians have had one. The United States has put five spacecraft into an orbit around the sun, while the Russians have put three spacecraft into orbit around the sun; the United States has orbited 181 spacecraft; the Russians 46.

As this is written, the United States has 89 spacecraft remaining in orbit while the comparable number for the Russians is only 12.

Condensed Log of Space Projects

NAME	INT'L DESIG.	PROJECT DIRECTION	LAUNCH DATA			WEIGHT
			Date[6]	Site	Vehicle	
Sputnik 1	1957 A 1	USSR	Oct 4, 1957			184
Sputnik 2	1957 B 1	USSR	Nov 3, 1957			1120
Vanguard TV 3[2]	None	USN	Dec 6, 1957	AMR	Vanguard	3
Explorer 1	1958 A 1	USA	Jan 31, 1958	AMR	Jupiter C	31
Vanguard TV 3[2] backup	None	USN	Feb 5, 1958	AMR	Vanguard	3
Explorer 2	None	USA	Mar 5, 1958	AMR	Jupiter C	32
Vanguard 1	1958 B 2	USN	Mar 17, 1958	AMR	Vanguard	3
Explorer 3	1958 Γ 1	USA	Mar 26, 1958	AMR	Jupiter C	31
Vanguard TV 5[2]	None	USN	Apr 28, 1958	AMR	Vanguard	22
Sputnik 3	1958 Δ 2	USSR	May 15, 1958			2925
Vanguard SLV 1[3]	None	USN	May 27, 1958	AMR	Vanguard	22
Vanguard SLV 2[3]	None	USN	June 26, 1958	AMR	Vanguard	22
Explorer 4	1958 E 1	ARPA	July 26, 1958	AMR	Jupiter C	38
Able 1 (Pioneer)	None	USAF	Aug 17, 1958	AMR	Thor-Able	84
Explorer 5	None	ARPA	Aug 24, 1958	AMR	Jupiter C	38
Vanguard SLV 3[3]	None	USN	Sept 26, 1958	AMR	Vanguard	22
Pioneer 1	None	NASA	Oct 11, 1958	AMR	Thor-Able	84
Beacon 1	None	NASA	Oct 23, 1958	AMR	Jupiter C	9
Pioneer 2	None	NASA	Nov 8, 1958	AMR	Thor-Able	87
Pioneer 3	None	NASA	Dec 6, 1958	AMR	Juno II	13
Score	1958 Z 1	ARPA	Dec 18, 1958	AMR	Atlas B	8750
Lunik 1	1959 M 1	USSR	Jan 2, 1959			3245
Vanguard 2	1959A 1	NASA	Feb 17, 1959	AMR	Vanguard	22
Discoverer 1	1959 B 1	ARPA	Feb 28, 1959	VAFB	Thor-Agena A	1300
Pioneer 4	1959 N 1	NASA	Mar 3, 1959	AMR	Juno II	13
Discoverer 2	1959 Γ 1	ARPA	Apr 13, 1959	VAFB	Thor-Agena A	1600
Vanguard SLV 5[3]	None	NASA	Apr 13, 1959	AMR	Vanguard	23
Discoverer 3	None	ARPA	June 3, 1959	VAFB	Thor-Agena A	1600
Vanguard SLV 6[3]	None	NASA	June 22, 1959	AMR	Vanguard	23
Discoverer 4	None	ARPA	June 25, 1959	VAFB	Thor-Agena A	1600
Explorer S-1	None	NASA	July 16, 1959	AMR	Juno II	92

AMR: Atlantic Missile Range
PA: Point Arguello
WI: Wallops Island
VAFB: Vandenberg AFB

[1]Current orbital data as of March 1, 1964
[2]TV: Test Vehicle
[3]SLV: Satellite Launching Vehicle
[4]Astronomical Unit
[5]Inclination from the ecliptic
[6]From local time at launch site

ORBITAL DATA INITIAL/CURRENT[1]				RESULTS
Period	Perigee	Apogee	Incl.	
96.2	141	588	65.1	Decayed 1-4-58: first artificial satellite, transmitted 21 days
103.7	140	1038	65.3	Decayed 4-14-58: carried dog Laika, transmitted 7 days
—	—	—	—	Failed to orbit: lost thrust after 2 seconds
114.7 104.8	224 214	1584 1012	33.3 33.2	In orbit: transmitted until 5-23-58, discovered radiation belt
—	—	—	—	Failed to orbit: control system malfunction
—	—	—	—	Failed to orbit: unsuccessful fourth stage ignition
134.3 134.1	405 393	2462 2462	34.3 34.2	In orbit: still transmitting in sunlight on 108.012 mc, proved earth pear-shaped
114.7	117	1739	33.5	Decayed 6-28-58: radiation and micrometeorite data until 6-16-58
—	—	—	—	Failed to orbit: third stage ignition malfunction
105.8	140	1168	65.2	Decayed 4-6-60: variety of data returned up to re-entry
—	—	—	—	Failed to orbit: improper third stage trajectory
—	—	—	—	Failed to orbit: premature second stage cutoff
110.1	163	1372	50.1	Decayed 10-23-59: mapped Project Argus radiation shells until 10-6-58
—	—	—	—	Lunar probe failed: first stage lox pump stopped
—	—	—	—	Failed to orbit: upper stages fired in wrong direction
—	—	—	—	Failed to orbit: insufficient second stage thrust
—	—	—	—	Lunar probe failed: third stage thrust insufficient; 70,717-mile altitude, returned radiation, magnetic field, micrometeorite data
—	—	—	—	Failed to orbit: upper stages separated prior to burnout
—	—	—	—	Lunar probe failed: third stage ignition unsuccessful
—	—	—	—	Lunar probe failed: early first stage cutoff; reached altitude of 63,580 miles, discovered outer portion of Van Allen radiation belt
101.5	115	914	32.3	Decayed 1-21-59: first comsat, relayed messages for 13 days
450 days	.9766AU[4]	1.315AU	0.01[5]	In solar orbit: lunar probe, passed within 4660 miles of moon
125.9 125.5	347 337	2064 2056	32.9 32.9	In orbit: transmitted for 18 days, returned first cloud cover photos
96.0	114	697	90.0	Decayed 3-5-59: first polar orbit, did not carry re-entry capsule
398 days	.9871AU[4]	1.142AU	1.30[5]	In solar orbit: lunar probe, passed within 37,300 miles of moon
90.6	152	225	90.0	Decayed 4-26-59: capsule ejected on orbit 17, lost in Arctic Ocean
—	—	—	—	Failed to orbit: second stage damaged at separation
—	—	—	—	Failed to orbit: second stage fired but no satellite signals received
—	—	—	—	Failed to orbit: second stage propulsion malfunction
—	—	—	—	Failed to orbit: insufficient second stage velocity
—	—	—	—	Failed to orbit: destroyed by range safety officer

Period: Minutes
Perigee and Apogee: statute miles
Inclination: degrees from the equator
Statute miles to kilometers: 1.609344
Statute to nautical miles: 0.86839

The Condensed Log section is compiled from the public announcements of the agencies responsible for project direction, the GSFC Satellite Situation Report and the UN. Some assumptions are made in correlating this information, therefore accuracy of the resulting data cannot be assured.

Condensed Log of Space Projects (Cont.)

NAME	INT'L DESIG.	PROJECT DIRECTION	LAUNCH DATA			WEIGHT
			Date	Site	Vehicle	
Explorer 6	1959 Δ 1	NASA	Aug 7, 1959	AMR	Thor-Able	143
Discoverer 5	1959 E 1	ARPA	Aug 13, 1959	VAFB	Thor-Agena A	1700
Beacon 2	None	NASA	Aug 14, 1959	AMR	Juno II	10
Discoverer 6	1959 Z 1	ARPA	Aug 19, 1959	VAFB	Thor-Agena A	1700
Lunik 2	1959 Ξ 1	USSR	Sept 12, 1959			858
Transit 1A	None	ARPA	Sept 17, 1959	AMR	Thor-Able	265
Vanguard 3	1959 E 1	NASA	Sept 18, 1959	AMR	Vanguard	100
Lunik 3	1959 Θ 1	USSR	Oct 4, 1959			614
Explorer 7	1959 I 1	NASA	Oct 13, 1959	AMR	Juno II	92
Discoverer 7	1959 K 1	ARPA	Nov 7, 1959	VAFB	Thor-Agena A	1700
Discoverer 8	1959 Λ 1	USAF	Nov 20, 1959	VAFB	Thor-Agena A	1700
Atlas-Able 4 (Pioneer)	None	NASA	Nov 26, 1959	AMR	Atlas-Able	372
Discoverer 9	None	USAF	Feb 4, 1960	VAFB	Thor-Agena A	1700
Discoverer 10	None	USAF	Feb 19, 1960	VAFB	Thor-Agena A	1700
Midas 1	None	USAF	Feb 26, 1960	AMR	Atlas-Agena A	4500
Pioneer 5	1960 A 1	NASA	Mar 11, 1960	AMR	Thor-Able	95
Explorer S-46	None	NASA	Mar 23, 1960	AMR	Juno II	35
Tiros 1	1960 B 2	NASA	Apr 1, 1960	AMR	Thor-Able	270
Transit 1B	1960 Γ 2	ARPA	Apr 13, 1960	AMR	Thor-Able Star	265
Discoverer 11	1960 Δ 1	USAF	Apr 15, 1960	VAFB	Thor-Agena A	1700
Echo A-10	None	NASA	May 13, 1960	AMR	Delta	132
Sputnik 4	1960 E 1	USSR	May 15, 1960			10,008
Midas 2	1960 Z 1	USAF	May 24, 1960	AMR	Atlas-Agena A	5000
Transit 2A	1960 H 1	USN	June 22, 1960	AMR	Thor-Able Star	223
Greb 1	1960 H 2					42
Discoverer 12	None	USAF	June 29, 1960	VAFB	Thor-Agena A	1700
Discoverer 13	1960 Θ 1	USAF	Aug 10, 1960	VAFB	Thor-Agena A	1700

[1]Current orbital data as of March 1, 1964

ORBITAL DATA INITIAL/CURRENT[1]				RESULTS
Period	Perigee	Apogee	Incl.	
768	157	26,366	47.0	Decayed 7-61: first use of solar paddles, transmitted until 10-6-59, discovered earth's electrical current system, returned first TV photo of earth
94.1	135	456	80.0	Decayed 9-28-59: capsule ejected into higher orbit on 16th pass
—	—	—	—	Failed to orbit: first stage fuel depletion, upper stage attitude control system malfunction
95.2	131	528	84.0	Decayed 10-20-59: capsule ejected on 17th orbit, recovery failed
Flight time: 33.5 hours				Impacted on moon: detected lunar ionosphere, no magnetic field or radiation
—	—	—	—	Failed to orbit: third stage ignition malfunction
130.2 / 129.9	317 / 318	2329 / 2315	33.3 / 33.3	In orbit: mapped earth's magnetic field, returned radiation and micrometeorite data until 12-11-59
16.2 days	25,257	291,439	76.8	Decayed 4-20-60: passed within 4373 miles of moon, photographed far side for 40 minutes from distance of 37,000-43,000 miles
101.2 / 101.2	346 / 343	676 / 669	50.3 / 50.3	In orbit: transmitted data on magnetic fields and storms, solar flares, radiation belt, micrometeorites until 8-24-61
94.6	99	519	81.6	Decayed 11-26-59: poor stabilization prevented capsule separation
103.7	120	1032	80.6	Decayed 3-8-60: capsule ejected 15th orbit, overshot recovery area
—	—	—	—	Lunar probe failed: payload shroud broke away after 45 seconds
—	—	—	—	Failed to orbit: premature first stage cutoff
—	—	—	—	Failed to orbit: destroyed by range safety officer
—	—	—	—	Failed to orbit: second stage failed to separate
312 days	.8061AU[4]	.995AU	3.35[5]	In solar orbit: interplanetary probe, returned data on magnetic field, solar wind, size of solar system, out to 22.5M miles (6-26-60)
—	—	—	—	Failed to orbit: apparent upper stage ignition malfunction
99.2 / 99.2	430 / 419	468 / 477	48.3 / 48.4	In orbit: first weather satellite, sent 22,952 photos up to 6-17-60
95.8 / 94.0	232 / 222	463 / 365	51.3 / 51.3	In orbit: first navigation satellite, ejected dummy pickaback payload, returned infrared data, transmitted until 7-12-60
92.3	103	375	80.1	Decayed 4-26-60: capule ejected on 17th orbit but not recovered
—	—	—	—	Failed to orbit: second stage attitude control malfunction
91.3	194	229	65.0	Decayed 9-5-62: fragment recovered in Wisconsin; Vostok prototype, cabin ejection attempted 5-19-60, separated into 8 pieces
94.4 / 94.4	299 / 297	321 / 311	33.0 / 33.0	In orbit: data link quit 2nd day, 67 micrometeorite impacts reported
101.7 / 101.6	389 / 381	665 / 655	66.7 / 66.7	In orbit: transmitted geodetic data until 8-62
101.6 / 101.6	382 / 381	657 / 654	66.8 / 66.7	In orbit: first pickaback, returned solar X-ray and UV data until 4-61
—	—	—	—	Failed to orbit: second stage attitude instability
94.1	157	431	82.8	Decayed 11-14-60: capsule recovered from ocean after ejection on orbit 17, first recovery of man-made object from space

[4]Astronomical Unit   [5]Inclination from the ecliptic

Condensed Log of Space Projects (Cont.)

NAME	INT'L DESIG.	PROJECT DIRECTION	LAUNCH DATA			WEIGHT
			Date	Site	Vehicle	
Echo 1	1960 I 1	NASA	Aug 12, 1960	AMR	Delta	166
Discoverer 14	1960 K 1	USAF	Aug 18, 1960	VAFB	Thor-Agena A	1700
Courier 1A	None	ARPA	Aug 18, 1960	AMR	Thor-Able Star	500
Sputnik 5	1960 Λ 1	USSR	Aug 19, 1960			10,120
Discoverer 15	1960 M 1	USAF	Sept 13, 1960	VAFB	Thor-Agena A	1700
Atlas-Able 5A (Pioneer)	None	NASA	Sept 25, 1960	AMR	Atlas-Able	387
Courier 1B	1960 N 1	USA	Oct 4, 1960	AMR	Thor-Able Star	500
None	None	USSR	Oct 10, 1960			
Samos 1	None	USAF	Oct 11, 1960	PA	Atlas-Agena A	4100
None	None	USSR	Oct 14, 1960			
Discoverer 16	None	USAF	Oct 26, 1960	VAFB	Thor-Agena B	2100
Explorer 8	1960 Ξ 1	NASA	Nov 3, 1960	AMR	Juno II	90
Discoverer 17	1960 O 1	USAF	Nov 12, 1960	VAFB	Thor-Agena B	2100
Tiros 2	1960 Π 1	NASA	Nov 23, 1960	AMR	Delta	280
Transit 3A/Greb 2	None	USN	Nov 30, 1960	AMR	Thor-Able Star	203/40
Sputnik 6	1960 P 1	USSR	Dec 1, 1960			10,060
Explorer S-56	None	NASA	Dec 4, 1960	WI	Scout	14
Discoverer 18	1960 Σ 1	USAF	Dec 7, 1960	VAFB	Thor-Agena B	2100
Atlas-Able 5B (Pioneer)	None	NASA	Dec 15, 1960	AMR	Atlas-Able	388
Discoverer 19	1960 T 1	USAF	Dec 20, 1960	VAFB	Thor-Agena B	2100
Samos 2	1961 A 1	USAF	Jan 31, 1961	PA	Atlas-Agena A	4100
Sputnik 7	1961 B 1	USSR	Feb 4, 1961			14,292
Venus Probe Sputnik 8	1961 Γ 1 1961 Γ 3	USSR	Feb 12, 1961			1419 14,292
Explorer 9	1961 Δ1	NASA	Feb 16, 1961	WI	Scout	15
Discoverer 20	1961 E 1	USAF	Feb 17, 1961	VAFB	Thor-Agena B	2450
Discoverer 21	1961 Z 1	USAF	Feb 18, 1961	VAFB	Thor-Agena B	2100
Transit 3B/Lofti 1	1961 H 1	USN	Feb 21, 1961	AMR	Thor-Able Star	250/57
Explorer S-45	None	NASA	Feb 24, 1961	AMR	Juno II	74
Sputnik 9	1961 Θ 1	USSR	Mar 9, 1961			10,340
Sputnik 10	1961 I 1	USSR	Mar 25, 1961			10,330

[1]Current orbital data as of March 1, 1964

ORBITAL DATA INITIAL/CURRENT[1]				RESULTS
Period	Perigee	Apogee	Incl.	
118.2 114.8	941 867	1052 991	47.2 47.3	In orbit: first passive comsat, relayed voice and crude TV signals
94.5	113	502	79.6	Decayed 9-16-60: capsule ejected 17th orbit, recovered in mid-air
—	—	—	—	Failed to orbit: launch vehicle exploded 2½ minutes after liftoff
90.7	190	211	64.9	Re-entered 8-20-60: cabin and capsule with dogs Belka and Strelka recovered on 18th orbit
94.2	125	469	80.9	Decayed 10-18-60: capsule ejected on 17th pass, sighted but not recovered
—	—	—	—	Lunar probe failed: second stage oxidizer system malfunction
106.9 107.1	586 603	767 756	28.3 28.3	In orbit: delayed and realtime communication tests made for 17 days
—	—	—	—	Mars probe failed
—	—	—	—	Failed to orbit: second stage ignited but did not go into orbit
—	—	—	—	Mars probe failed
—	—	—	—	Failed to orbit: second stage, booster failed to separate
112.7 112.4	285 260	1422 1399	50.0 50.0	In orbit: transmitted data on ionosphere until 12-28-60
96.4	113	614	81.9	Decayed 12-29-60: capsule separated 31st orbit, mid-air recovery
98.3 98.3	387 382	452 458	48.5 48.5	In orbit: returned 36,156 cloud cover photos until 12-4-61
—	—	—	—	Failed to orbit: destroyed by range safety officer
88.6	116	165	65.0	Decayed 12-2-60: re-entry cabin with dogs Pchelka and Mushka burned up as recovery attempt failed
—	—	—	—	Failed to orbit: second stage ignition malfunction
93.8	143	426	80.8	Decayed 4-2-61: capsule recovered in mid-air on 48th orbit
—	—	—	—	Lunar probe failed: exploded 70 seconds after liftoff
93.0	128	390	82.8	Decayed 1-23-61: carried infrared experiments, no re-entry capsule
95.0 94.7	300 290	350 334	97.0 97.4	In orbit: returned micrometeorite impact data
89.8	139	204	65.0	Decayed 2-26-61: believed to be Venus probe abort
300 days 89.7	.7183AU[4] 123	1.0190AU 198	0.58[5] 65.0	In solar orbit: Venus probe, radio contact lost at 4.7M miles Decayed 2-25-61: launched Venus probe from parking orbit
118.3 105.5	395 206	1605 1058	38.6 39.0	In orbit: optical tracking of 12-foot balloon correlated upper atmosphere density with solar activity
95.4	177	486	80.4	Decayed 7-28-62: programmer failure prevented capsule ejection
93.8	149	659	80.7	Decayed 4-20-62: carried infrared experiments, no re-entry capsule
94.5	117	511	28.4	Decayed 3-30-61: second stage and satellites failed to separate
—	—	—	—	Failed to orbit: third and fourth stage ignition malfunction
88.5	114	155	64.9	Re-entered 3-9-61: cabin with dog Chernushka recovered
88.4	111	153	64.9	Re-entered 3-26-61: cabin with dog Zvezdochka recovered after 17 orbits

[4]Astronomical Unit   [5]Inclination from the ecliptic

Condensed Log of Space Projects (Cont.)

NAME	INT'L DESIG.	PROJECT DIRECTION	LAUNCH DATA			WEIGHT
			Date	Site	Vehicle	
Explorer 10	1961 K 1	NASA	Mar 25, 1961	AMR	Delta	79
Discoverer 22	None	USAF	Mar 30, 1961	VAFB	Thor-Agena B	2100
Discoverer 23	1961 Λ 1	USAF	Apr 8, 1961	VAFB	Thor-Agena B	2100
Vostok 1	1961 M 1	USSR	Apr 12, 1961	"Baikonur"		10,418
Mercury-Atlas 3	None	NASA	Apr 25, 1961	AMR	Atlas D	2000
Explorer 11	1961 N 1	NASA	Apr 27, 1961	AMR	Juno II	82
Explorer S-45A	None	NASA	May 24, 1961	AMR	Juno II	75
Discoverer 24	None	USAF	June 8, 1961	VAFB	Thor-Agena B	2100
Discoverer 25	1961 Ξ 1	USAF	June 16, 1961	VAFB	Thor-Agena B	2100
Transit 4A	1961 O 1	USN	June 29, 1961	AMR	Thor-Able Star	175
Injun 1/Greb 3	1961 O 2					55/40
Explorer S-55	None	NASA	June 30, 1961	WI	Scout	187
Discoverer 26	1961 II 1	USAF	July 7, 1961	VAFB	Thor-Agena B	2100
Tiros 3	1961 P 1	NASA	July 12, 1961	AMR	Delta	285
Midas 3	1961 Σ 1	USAF	July 12, 1961	PA	Atlas-Agena B	3500
Discoverer 27	None	USAF	July 21, 1961	VAFB	Thor-Agena B	2100
Discoverer 28	None	USAF	Aug 3, 1961	VAFB	Thor-Agena B	2100
Vostok 2	1961 T 1	USSR	Aug 6, 1961	"Baikonur"		10,430
Explorer 12	1961 Υ 1	NASA	Aug 15, 1961	AMR	Delta	82
Ranger 1	1961 Φ 1	NASA	Aug 23, 1961	AMR	Atlas-Agena B	675
Explorer 13	1961 X 1	NASA	Aug 25, 1961	WI	Scout	187
Discoverer 29	1961 Ψ 1	USAF	Aug 30, 1961	VAFB	Thor-Agena B	2100
Samos 3	None	USAF	Sept 9, 1961	PA	Atlas-Agena B	4200
Discoverer 30	1961 Ω 1	USAF	Sept 12, 1961	VAFB	Thor-Agena B	2100
Mercury-Atlas 4	1961 AA 1	NASA	Sept 13, 1961	AMR	Atlas D	2700
Discoverer 31	1961 AB 1	USAF	Sept 17, 1961	VAFB	Thor-Agena B	2100
Discoverer 32	1961 AΓ 1	USAF	Oct 13, 1961	VAFB	Thor-Agena B	2100
Midas 4	1961 AΔ 1	USAF	Oct 21, 1961	PA	Atlas Agena B	3500
Discoverer 33	None	USAF	Oct 23, 1961	VAFB	Thor-Agena B	2100
Mercury-Scout 1	None	NASA	Nov 1, 1961	AMR	Scout	150
Discoverer 34	1961 AE 1	USAF	Nov 5, 1961	VAFB	Thor-Agena B	2100
Discoverer 35	1961 AZ 1	USAF	Nov 15, 1961	VAFB	Thor-Agena B	2100
Transit 4B	1961 AH 1	USN	Nov 15, 1961	AMR	Thor-Able Star	190
Traac	1961 AH 2					240

ORBITAL DATA INITIAL/CURRENT[1]				RESULTS
Period	Perigee	Apogee	Incl.	
112 hrs	100	145,000	33.0	Position uncertain: magnetic fields, solar wind data for two days
—	—	—	—	Failed to orbit: second stage control system malfunction
101.2	126	882	81.9	Decayed 4-16-62: capsule ejected into separate orbit, no recovery
89.1	112	203	65.0	Re-entered 4-12-61: cabin with Y. Gagarin recovered after 1 orbit
—	—	—	—	Failed to orbit: destroyed by range safety officer
108.1	304	1113	28.8	In orbit: gamma ray counter returned data until 12-6-61
108.0	313	1099	28.8	
—	—	—	—	Failed to orbit: second stage ignition malfunction
—	—	—	—	Failed to orbit: second stage ignition malfunction
90.9	139	251	82.1	Decayed 7-12-61: capsule recovered from ocean after 33 orbits
103.7	534	623	67.0	In orbit: first nuclear power supply, transmitted until 5-63
103.8	546	618	66.8	
103.8	534	634	67.0	In orbit: failed to separate, Injun provided radiation data until
103.8	546	619	66.8	3-6-63; Greb relayed solar X-ray data until late 1961
—	—	—	—	Failed to orbit: third stage ignition malfunction
95.0	146	503	82.9	Decayed 12-5-61: capsule recovered in mid-air on 32nd orbit
100.4	461	506	47.8	In orbit: returned 35,033 photos up to 2-27-62
100.4	462	506	47.9	
160.0	1850	1850	91.1	In orbit: first Midas launch from Point Arguello
161.4	2066	2212	91.1	
—	—	—	—	Failed to orbit: destroyed by range safety officer
—	—	—	—	Failed to orbit: second stage control system malfunction
88.6	111	160	64.9	Re-entered 8-7-61: cabin, G. Titov landed separately, 17 orbits
1585	182	48,000	33.3	In orbit: returned radiation, solar wind data until 12-6-61
91.1	105	313	32.9	Decayed 8-30-61: attempt to reach deep space orbit failed
97.3	175	606	36.4	Decayed 8-28-61: orbit lower than planned, little useful data returned
91.0	140	345	82.1	Decayed 9-10-61: capsule ejected on 33rd orbit, recovered from ocean
—	—	—	—	Failed to orbit: exploded on launch pad
92.4	154	345	82.6	Decayed 12-11-61: capsule recovered in mid-air on 33rd orbit
88.6	100	159	32.6	Re-entered 9-13-61: recovered from ocean after 1 orbit
91.0	152	255	82.7	Decayed 10-26-61: re-entry capsule separation attempt failed
90.8	147	246	81.7	Decayed 11-13-61: mid-air capsule recovery after 18 orbits
172.0				In orbit: West Ford cannister ejected but dipoles failed
165.9	2189	2315	95.9	to separate
—	—	—	—	Failed to orbit: launch vehicle shut down prematurely
—	—	—	—	Failed to orbit: first stage exploded after 26 seconds
97.2	134	637	82.7	Decayed 12-7-62: system malfunction prevented capsule ejection
89.8	147	173	81.6	Decayed 12-3-61: capsule ejected on 18th orbit, recovered in mid-air
105.6	582	700	32.4	In orbit: returned geodetic data, ceased transmitting 8-62
105.9	590	695	32.4	
105.6	562	720	32.4	In orbit: orientation experiment failed, returned radiation data
105.9	599	688	32.4	until 8-62

[1]Current orbital data as of March 1, 1964

Condensed Log of Space Projects (Cont.)

NAME	INT'L DESIG.	PROJECT DIRECTION	LAUNCH DATA			WEIGHT
			Date	Site	Vehicle	
Ranger 2	1961 AΘ 1	NASA	Nov 18, 1961	AMR	Atlas-Agena B	675
None	None	USAF	Nov 22, 1961	PA	Atlas-Agena B	
Mercury-Atlas 5	1961 AI 1	NASA	Nov 29, 1961	AMR	Atlas D	2900
Discoverer 36	1961 AK 1	USAF	Dec 12, 1961	VAFB	Thor-Agena B	2100
Oscar 1	1961 AK 2					10
None	1961 AΛ 1	USAF	Dec 22, 1961	PA	Atlas-Agena B	
Discoverer 37	None	USAF	Jan 13, 1962	VAFB	Thor-Agena B	2100
Composite 1	None	USN	Jan 24, 1962	AMR	Thor-Able Star	219
Ranger 3	1962 A 1	NASA	Jan 26, 1962	AMR	Atlas-Agena B	727
Tiros 4	1962 B 1	NASA	Feb 8, 1962	AMR	Delta	285
Mercury-Atlas 6	1962 Γ 1	NASA	Feb 20, 1962	AMR	Atlas D	2987
None	1962 Δ 1	USAF	Feb 21, 1962	VAFB	Thor-Agena B	
Discoverer 38	1962 E 1	USAF	Feb 27, 1962	VAFB	Thor-Agena B	2100
OSO 1	1962 Z 1	NASA	Mar 7, 1962	AMR	Delta	458
None	1962 H 1	USAF	Mar 7, 1962	PA	Atlas-Agena B	
Cosmos 1	1962 Θ 1	USSR	Mar 16, 1962	Kapustin Yar		
Cosmos 2	1962 I 1	USSR	Apr 6, 1962	Kapustin Yar		
None	1962 K 1	USAF	Apr 9, 1962	PA	Atlas-Agena B	
None	1962 Λ 1	USAF	Apr 17, 1962	VAFB	Thor-Agena B	
Ranger 4	1962 M 1	NASA	Apr 23, 1962	AMR	Atlas-Agena B	730
Cosmos 3	1962 N 1	USSR	Apr 24, 1962	Kapustin Yar		
Cosmos 4	1962 Ξ 1	USSR	Apr 26, 1962	Tyuratam		
Ariel (UK 1)	1962 O 1	NASA/UK	Apr 26, 1962	AMR	Delta	132
None	None	USAF	Apr 26, 1962	PA	Scout	
None	1962 Π 1	USAF	Apr 26, 1962	PA	Atlas-Agena B	
None	1962 P 1	USAF	Apr 28, 1962	VAFB	Thor-Agena B	
Anna 1A	None	USN	May 10, 1962	AMR	Thor-Able Star	355
None	1962 Σ 1	USAF	May 15, 1962	VAFB	Thor-Agena B	
None	None	USAF	May 23, 1962	PA	Scout	

[1]Current orbital data as of March 1, 1964

ORBITAL DATA INITIAL/CURRENT[1]				RESULTS
Period	Perigee	Apogee	Incl.	
88.3	98	147	33.3	Decayed 11-18-61: attempt to reach deep space orbit failed
—	—	—	—	Failed to orbit: classified payload
88.5	100	148	32.5	Re-entered 11-29-61: chimp Enos recovered after 3 orbits
91.5	148	280	81.2	Decayed 3-8-62: capsule ejected on 64th orbit, recovered from ocean
91.1	146	258	81.2	Decayed 1-31-62: first amateur satellite, transmitted for 18 days
94.5	145	467	89.6	Decayed 8-14-62: classified payload (initial orbital data as of 2-15-62)
—	—	—	—	Failed to orbit: malfunction following second stage ignition
—	—	—	—	Failed to orbit: insufficient second stage thrust, carried 5 satellites
406.4 days	.9839AU[4]	1.163AU	.3988[5]	In solar orbit: lunar probe, missed moon by 22,862 miles
100.4	441	525	48.3	In orbit: returned total of 32,593 cloud cover
100.4	439	526	48.3	photos up to 6-10-62
88.5	100	163	32.5	Re-entered 2-20-62: "Friendship 7" with J. Glenn recovered after 3 orbits, first U.S. manned orbital mission
89.7	104	233	82.0	Decayed 3-4-62: classified payload (initial orbital data as of 2-27-62)
89.7	208	308	82.2	Decayed 3-21-62: capsule recovered in mid-air after 65 orbits (initial orbital data as of 3-13-62)
96.2	344	370	32.8	In orbit: transmitted solar flare, radiation data until 8-6-63,
96.1	346	365	32.8	first observatory-class spacecraft
93.9	147	428	90.9	Decayed 6-7-63: classified payload (initial orbital data as of 3-13-62)
96.4	135	609	49.0	Decayed 5-25-62: unannounced payload
102.0	131	960	49.0	Decayed 8-19-63: unannounced payload
153.0	1731	2116	86.7	In orbit: classified payload (initial orbital data as of 4-10-62)
152.9	1732	2114	86.7	
91.5	98	333	73.5	Decayed 5-28-62: classified payload (initial orbital data as of 4-30-62)
Flight time: 64.0 hours				Impacted on moon: experiments inoperative due to timer failure
93.8	142	447	49.0	Decayed 10-17-62: unannounced payload
90.6	184	205	65.0	Re-entered or decayed 4-29-62: unannounced payload
100.9	242	754	53.9	In orbit: first NASA international satellite, transmitting on
100.6	245	732	53.8	136.406 mc
—	—	—	—	Failed to orbit: classified payload
				Decayed 4-28-62: classified payload
91.1	98	307	73.2	Decayed 5-26-62: classified payload (initial orbital data as of 4-30-62)
—	—	—	—	Failed to orbit: second stage ignition malfunction
94.0	180	401	82.5	Decayed 11-26-63: classified payload (initial orbital data as of 5-17-62)
—	—	—	—	Failed to orbit: classified payload

[4]Astronomical Unit   [5]Inclination from the ecliptic

Condensed Log of Space Projects (Cont.)

NAME	INT'L DESIG.	PROJECT DIRECTION	LAUNCH DATA			WEIGHT
			Date	Site	Vehicle	
Mercury-Atlas 7	1962 τ 1	NASA	May 24, 1962	AMR	Atlas D	2975
Cosmos 5	1962 τ 1	USSR	May 28, 1962	Kapustin Yar		
None	1962 Φ 1	USAF	May 29, 1962	VAFB	Thor-Agena B	
None Oscar 2	1962 X 1 1962 X 2	USAF	June 2, 1962	VAFB	Thor-Agena B	10
None	1962 Ψ 1	USAF	June 17, 1962	PA	Atlas-Agena B	
None	1962 Ω 1	USAF	June 18, 1962	VAFB	Thor-Agena B	
Tiros 5	1962 AA 1	NASA	June 19, 1962	AMR	Delta	286
None	1962 AB 1	USAF	June 22, 1962	VAFB	Thor-Agena B	
None	1962 AΓ 1	USAF	June 27, 1962	VAFB	Thor-Agena D	
Cosmos 6	1962 AΔ 1	USSR	June 30, 1962	Kapustin Yar		
Telstar 1	1962 AE 1	AT&T	July 10, 1962	AMR	Delta	170
None	1962 AZ 1	USAF	July 18, 1962	PA	Atlas-Agena B	
None	1962 AH 1	USAF	July 20, 1962	VAFB	Thor-Agena B	
Mariner 1	None	NASA	July 22, 1962	AMR	Atlas Agena B	446
None	1962 AΘ 1	USAF	July 28, 1962	VAFB	Thor-Agena B	
Cosmos 7	1962 AI 1	USSR	July 28, 1962	Tyuratam		
None	1962 AK 1	USAF	Aug 1, 1962	VAFB	Thor-Agena D	
None	1962 AΛ 1	USAF	Aug 5, 1962	PA	Atlas-Agena B	
Vostok 3	1962 AM 1	USSR	Aug 11, 1962	Tyuratam		10,362
Vostok 4	1962 AN 1	USSR	Aug 12, 1962	Tyuratam		10,362
Cosmos 8	1962 AΞ 1	USSR	Aug 18, 1962	Kapustin Yar		
None	1962 AO 1	USAF	Aug 23, 1962	PA	Scout	
None	1962 AΠ 1	USSR	Aug 25, 1962			
Mariner 2	1962 AP 1	NASA	Aug 26, 1962	AMR	Atlas-Agena B	447
None	1962 AΣ 1	USAF	Aug 28, 1962	VAFB	Thor-Agena D	
None	1962 AT 1	USSR	Sept 1, 1962			

[1]Current orbital data as of March 1, 1964

| ORBITAL DATA INITIAL/CURRENT[1] | | | | RESULTS |
Period	Perigee	Apogee	Incl.	
88.3	100	167	32.5	Re-entered 5-24-62: "Aurora 7" and S. Carpenter recovered, 3 orbits
102.8	126	994	49.1	Decayed 5-2-63: unannounced payload
89.9	121	212	74.1	Decayed 6-11-62: classified payload (initial orbital data as of 5-31-62)
90.5	131	241	74.3	Decayed 6-28-62: classified payload (initial orbital data as of 6-5-62)
90.5	129	240	74.3	Decayed 6-21-62: amateur radio satellite transmitted 18 days
				Decayed 6-18-62: classified payload
92.3	234	244	82.0	Decayed 10-29-63: classified payload (initial orbital data as of 6-19-62)
100.5 100.5	367 364	604 606	58.1 58.1	In orbit: returned 57,857 cloud cover photos until 5-4-63
89.0	130	150	75.1	Decayed 7-7-62: classified payload (initial orbital data as of 6-30-62)
93.6	131	398	76.0	Decayed 9-14-62: classified payload (initial orbital data as of 6-30-62)
90.1	168	221	48.9	Decayed 8-8-62: unannounced payload
157.8 157.8	593 592	3503 3504	44.8 44.8	In orbit: first active repeater comsat, transmitted until 2-21-63
				Decayed 7-27-62: classified payload
90.0	122	218	70.3	Decayed 8-14-62: classified payload (initial orbital data as of 7-31-62
—	—	—	—	Venus probe failed: destroyed by range safety officer
90.7	129	251	71.1	Decayed 8-24-62: classified payload (initial orbital data as of 7-31-62)
90.1	130	229	65.0	Re-entered or decayed 8-1-62: unannounced payload
90.2	121	227	82.3	Decayed 8-26-62: classified payload (initial orbital data as of 8-14-62)
				Decayed 8-6-62: classified payload
88.3	114	156	65.0	Re-entered 8-15-62: cabin and A. Nikoloyev landed separately after 64 orbits
88.4	112	158	65.0	Re-entered 8-15-62: cabin and P. Popovich landed separately after 48 orbits, 6 minutes after Vostok 3 re-entry; initial orbit placed Vostok 4 within 3.1 miles of Vostok 3
92.9	159	375	49.0	Decayed 8-17-63: unannounced payload
99.6 99.5	388 380	526 532	98.6 98.7	In orbit: classified payload (initial orbital data as of 8-31-62)
99.6	390	526	98.6	Decayed 8-28-62: probable Venus probe failure
348 days	.7046AU[4]	1.229AU	1.66[5]	In solar orbit: passed within 21,594 miles of Venus, returned data out to 54.3M miles (1-3-63)
90.4	114	250	65.2	Decayed 9-10-62: classified payload (initial orbital data as of 8-31-62)
				Decayed 9-6-62: probable Venus probe failure

[4]Astronomical Unit   [5]Inclination from the ecliptic

Condensed Log of Space Projects (Cont.)

NAME	INT'L DESIG.	PROJECT DIRECTION	Date	Site	Vehicle	WEIGHT
			LAUNCH DATA			
None	1962 AΥ 1	USAF	Sept 1, 1962	VAFB	Thor-Agena B	
None	1962 AΦ 1	USSR	Sept 12, 1962			
None/TRS 1	1962 AX 1	USAF	Sept 17, 1962	VAFB	Thor-Agena B	/1.5
Tiros 6	1962 AΨ 1	NASA	Sept 18, 1962	AMR	Delta	281
Cosmos 9	1962 AΩ 1	USSR	Sept 27, 1962	Tyuratam		
Alouette 1	1962 BA 1	Canada	Sept 28, 1962	VAFB	Thor-Agena B	320
None	1962 BB 1	USAF	Sept 29, 1962	VAFB	Thor-Agena D	
Explorer 14	1962 BΓ 1	NASA	Oct 2, 1962	AMR	Delta	89
Mercury-Atlas 8	1962 BΔ 1	NASA	Oct 3, 1962	AMR	Atlas D	3030
None	1962 BE 1	USAF	Oct 9, 1962	VAFB	Thor-Agena B	
Cosmos 10	1962 BZ 1	USSR	Oct 17, 1962	Tyuratam		
Ranger 5	1962 BH 1	NASA	Oct 18, 1962	AMR	Atlas-Agena B	755
Cosmos 11	1962 BΘ 1	USSR	Oct 20, 1962	Kapustin Yar		
None	1962 BI 1	USSR	Oct 24, 1962			
Starad	1962 BK 1	USAF	Oct 26, 1962	VAFB	Thor-Agena D	
Explorer 15	1962 BΛ 1	NASA	Oct 27, 1962	AMR	Delta	98
Anna 1B	1962 BM 1	USN	Oct 31, 1962	AMR	Thor-Able Star	350
Mars 1	1962 BN 3	USSR	Nov 1, 1962			1965
None	1962 BΞ 1	USSR	Nov 4, 1962			
None	1962 BO 1	USAF	Nov 5, 1962	VAFB	Thor-Agena B	
None	1962 BΠ 1	USAF	Nov 11, 1962	PA	Atlas-Agena B	
None	1962 BP 1	USAF	Nov 24, 1962	VAFB	Thor-Agena B	
None	1962 BΣ 1	USAF	Dec 4, 1962	VAFB	Thor-Agena D	
None	1962 BT 1					
Injun 3	1962 BT 2					114
None	1962 BT 3	USAF/USN	Dec 12, 1962	VAFB	Thor-Agena D	
None	1962 BT 4					
None	1962 BT 5					

[1]Current orbital data as of March 1, 1964

ORBITAL, DATA INITIAL/CURRENT[1]				RESULTS
Period	**Perigee**	**Apogee**	**Incl.**	
94.4 92.0	189 172	418 289	82.8 82.8	In orbit: classified payload (initial orbital data as of 9-15-62)
				Decayed 9-14-62: probable Venus probe failure
92.8	124	383	81.9	Decayed 11-19-62: classified payload, failed to eject TRS pickaback which returned solar cell damage data (initial orbital data as of 9-30-62)
98.7 98.7	423 423	444 444	58.2 58.3	In orbit: detected 13 hurricanes, returned 67,000 cloud cover photos until 10-11-63
90.0	187	220	65.0	Re-entered or decayed 10-1-62: unannounced payload
105.4 105.4	620 616	638 644	80.5 80.5	In orbit: ionosphere sounding satellite, transmitting on 136.592, 136.978, 136.077 mc
90.3	119	241	65.4	Decayed 10-14-62: classified payload (initial orbital data as of 9-30-62)
2184 2185	174 1616	61,190 59,769	32.9 42.8	In orbit: energetic particles satellite, transmitted until 10-8-63
89.0	100	176	32.5	Re-entered 10-3-62: "Sigma 7" with W. Schirra recovered within 5 miles of carrier after 6 orbits
90.9	103	291	81.5	Decayed 11-16-62: classified payload (initial orbital data as of 10-10-62)
90.2	130	236	65.0	Re-entered or decayed 10-21-62: unannounced payload
366 days	.9490AU[4]	1.052AU	.3901[5]	In solar orbit: lunar probe, missed moon by 450 miles
96.1 91.4	152 134	572 291	49.0 49.0	In orbit: anannounced payload
				Decayed 10-29-62: probable Mars probe failure
147.8 136.8	120 122	3452 2941	71.4 71.3	In orbit: payload returned Starfish radiation data until 1-18-63
312.0 312.8	194 193	10,760 10,851	18.0 18.0	In orbit: excessive spin rate degraded radiation data, transmitted until 2-9-63
107.8 107.9	670 662	728 743	50.1 50.2	In orbit: flash tubes operational, transmitting on 162, 324 mc
519 days	.9237AU[4]	1.604AU	2.683[5]	In solar orbit: Mars probe transmissions ceased after 66M miles
				Decayed 11-5-62: probable Mars probe failure
90.7	130	250	75.0	Decayed 12-3-62: classified payload (initial orbital data as of 11-7-62)
				Decayed 11-12-62: classified payload
89.8	129	202	65.2	Decayed 12-13-62: classified payload (initial orbital data as of 11-30-62)
89.2	119	175	65.0	Decayed 12-8-62: classified payload (initial orbital data as of 12-6-62)
116.0 111.3	153 141	1724 1458	70.4 70.4	In orbit: classified payload (initial orbital data as of 12-15-62)
116.3 113.5	153 145	1729 1581	70.3 70.4	In orbit: transmitted radiation data until 11-3-63
115.6	139	1700	70.3	Decayed 7-1-63: classified pickaback
116.2 108.8	145 140	1728 1314	70.4 70.4	In orbit: classified pickaback
116.0 111.2	146 150	1718 1444	70.3 70.3	In orbit: classified pickaback

[4]Astronomical Unit   [5]Inclination from the ecliptic

Condensed Log of Space Projects (Cont.)

NAME	INT'L DESIG.	PROJECT DIRECTION	LAUNCH DATA			WEIGHT
			Date	Site	Vehicle	
Relay 1	1962 BΥ 1	NASA	Dec 13, 1962	AMR	Delta	172
None	1962 BΦ 1	USAF	Dec 14, 1962	VAFB	Thor-Agena D	
Explorer 16	1962 BX 1	NASA	Dec 16, 1962	WI	Scout	222
None	None	USAF	Dec 17, 1962	PA	Atlas-Agena B	
Transit 5A	1962 BΨ 1	USN	Dec 18, 1962	PA	Scout	135
Cosmos 12	1962 BΩ 1	USSR	Dec 22, 1962	Tyuratam		
None	1963 1A[7]	USSR	Jan 4, 1963			
None	1963 2A	USAF	Jan 7, 1963	VAFB	Thor-Agena D	
None	1963 3A	USAF	Jan 16, 1963	VAFB	Thor-Agena D	
Syncom 1	1963 4A	NASA	Feb 14, 1963	AMR	Delta	86
None	1963 5A	USAF	Feb 19, 1963	PA	Scout	
None	None	USAF	Feb 28, 1963	VAFB	[8]TAT-Agena D	
None	None	USAF	Mar 18, 1963	VAFB	TAT-Agena D	
Cosmos 13	1963 6A	USSR	Mar 20, 1963	Tyuratam		
None	1963 7A	USAF	Apr 1, 1963	VAFB	Thor-Agena D	
Lunik 4	1963 8B	USSR	Apr 2, 1963			3135
Explorer 17	1963 9A	NASA	Apr 2, 1963	AMR	Delta	405
None	None	USAF	Apr 5, 1963	PA	Scout	
Cosmos 14	1963 10A	USSR	Apr 13, 1963	Kapustin Yar		
Cosmos 15	1963 11A	USSR	Apr 22, 1963	Tyuratam		
None	None	USAF	Apr 26, 1963	PA	Scout	
None	None	USAF	Apr 26, 1963	VAFB	Thor-Agena D	
Cosmos 16	1963 12A	USSR	Apr 28, 1963	Tyuratam		
Telstar 2	1963 13A	AT&T	May 7, 1963	AMR	Delta	175

[1]Current orbital data as of March 1, 1964

| ORBITAL DATA INITIAL/CURRENT[7] | | | | RESULTS |
Period	Perigee	Apogee	Incl.	
185.9 185.1	819 820	4612 4624	47.5 47.5	In orbit: active repeater comsat, transmitting on 136.140, 136.620 mc
90.5	126	241	70.0	Decayed 1-8-62: classified payload (initial orbital data as of 12-15-62)
104.4 104.4	466 461	733 739	52.0 52.0	In orbit: transmitted until 7-22-63, provided first statistically significant meteoroid penetration data
—	—	—	—	Failed to orbit: classified payload
99.2 99.0	432 424	455 460	90.7 90.6	In orbit: power supply malfunction after 1 day
90.5	131	252	65.0	Re-entered or decayed 12-30-62: unannounced payload
				Decayed 1-5-63: probable lunar probe failure
90.5	130	244	82.0	Decayed 1-24-63: classified payload
94.7 94.4	297 281	322 330	82.0 81.9	In orbit: classified payload
1426.6	21,195	22,953	33.5	In orbit: communication lost at injection into synchronous orbit
97.8 97.6	304 309	496 494	100.5 100.5	In orbit: classified payload
—	—	—	—	Failed to orbit: classified payload, first use of thrust-augmented Thor
—	—	—	—	Failed to orbit: classified payload
89.8	127	209	65.0	Re-entered or decayed 3-29-63: unannounced payload
90.6	129	254	75.4	Decayed 4-26-63: classified payload
	55,800	434,000		In orbit: lunar probe, missed moon by 5281 miles, now in barycentric orbit
96.4 95.4	158 156	568 512	57.6 57.6	In orbit: atmospheric structure satellite, transmitted until 7-10-63, first measurement of neutral hydrogen belt
—	—	—	—	Failed to orbit: classified payload
92.1	165	318	48.6	Decayed 8-29-63: unannounced payload
89.8	107	231	65.0	Re-entered or decayed 4-27-63: unannounced payload
—	—	—	—	Failed to orbit: classified payload
—	—	—	—	Failed to orbit: classified payload
90.4	129	249	65.0	Re-entered or decayed 5-8-63: unannounced payload
225.0 225.3	604 602	6713 6715	42.7 42.7	In orbit: active repeater comsat, silent from 7-15 to 8-12-63, now transmitting on 136.050 mc

[7] New international designation system initiated 1-1-63   [8] Thrust Augmented Thor

Condensed Log of Space Projects (Cont.)

| NAME | INT'L DESIG. | PROJECT DIRECTION | LAUNCH DATA | | | WEIGHT |
			Date	Site	Vehicle	
None	1963 14A					
TRS 2	1963 14B	USAF	May 9, 1963	PA	Atlas-Agena B	1.5
TRS 3	1963 14C					1.5
Mercury-Atlas 9	1963 15A	NASA	May 15, 1963	AMR	Atlas D	3000
None	1963 16A	USAF	May 18, 1963	VAFB	Thor-Agena D	
Cosmos 17	1963 17A	USSR	May 22, 1963	Kapustin Yar		
Cosmos 18	1963 18A	USSR	May 24, 1963	Tyuratam		
None	None	USAF	June 12, 1963	PA	Atlas-Agena B	
None	1963 19A	USAF	June 12, 1963	VAFB	Thor-Agena D	
Vostok 5	1963 20A	USSR	June 14, 1963	Tyuratam		10,362
Lofti 2A Greb 4 Radose None Surcal 1B	1963 21B 1963 21C 1963 21D 1963 21E 1963 21F	USAF/USN	June 15, 1963	·VAFB	Thor-Agena D	
None	1963 22A	USAF	June 15, 1963	PA	Scout	
Vostok 6	1963 23A	USSR	June 16, 1963	Tyuratam		10,362
Tiros 7	1963 24A	NASA	June 19, 1963	AMR	Delta	297
None Hitch-hiker 1	1963 25A 1963 25B	USAF	June 26, 1963	VAFB	Thor-Agena D	176
Geophysical Research Satellite	1963 26A	USAF	June 28, 1963	WI	Scout	
None	1963 27A	USAF	June 29, 1963	VAFB	Thor-Agena B	
None	1963 28A	USAF	July 12, 1963	PA	Atlas-Agena D	
None	1963 29A	USAF	July 18, 1963	VAFB	Thor-Agena D	
None TRS 4 None	1963 30A 1963 30B 1963 30D	USAF	July 19, 1963	VAFB	Atlas-Agena B	1.5

ORBITAL, DATA INITIAL/CURRENT[1]				RESULTS
Period	Perigee	Apogee	Incl.	
166.6	2249	2290	87.4	In orbit: classified payload, ejected 50-pound package of West
166.4	2238	2289	87.3	Ford copper dipoles, communication tests successful
166.5	2241	2297	87.4	In orbit: radiation pickaback returned data for 92 days
166.4	2231	2295	87.4	
166.5	2238	2282	87.3	In orbit: radiation pickaback returned data for 89 days
166.4	2252	2274	87.4	
88.5	100	166	32.5	Re-entered 5-16-63: "Faith 7" with G. Cooper recovered after 22 orbits, within 4 miles of carrier USS Kearsarge
				Decayed 5-27-63: classified payload
94.8	162	490	49.0	In orbit: unannounced payload
93.6	162	396	49.0	
89.4	130	187	65.0	Re-entered or decayed 6-2-63: unannounced payload
—	—	—	—	Failed to orbit: classified payload
90.7	127	263	81.9	Decayed 7-12-63: classified payload
88.3	109	138	65.0	Re-entered 6-19-63: cabin, V. Bykovsky landed after 82 orbits
95.2	109	550	69.9	Decayed 7-18-63: VLF experiment
95.1	109	546	69.9	Decayed 8-1-63: solar radiation payload
95.2	109	549	69.9	Decayed 7-30-63: radiation dosimeter payload
95.0	109	541	69.9	Decayed 7-27-63: classified payload
94.9	114	533	69.9	Decayed 7-5-63: surveillance calibration payload
100.7	463	528	90.0	In orbit: classified payload, transmitting on 150, 400 mc,
99.6	456	465	90.0	gravity gradient stabilization system successfully deployed
88.4	114	145	65.0	Re-entered 6-19-63: cabin and V. Tereshkova landed separately after 49 orbits, 3 hours before Vostok 5 landing
97.4	385	401	58.2	In orbit: wide angle cameras, IR experiments operating,
97.4	389	400	58.2	transmissions on 136.234, 136.922 mc
90.1	126	255	80.8	Decayed 7-26-63: classified payload
132.6	201	2571	82.1	In orbit: pickaback to measure artificial radiation decay,
132.3	214	2551	82.2	returned good data on solar flares, low energy particles
102.1	267	808	49.8	In orbit: carried two experiments to measure space gas
102.1	258	809	49.7	composition, telemetry returned for 13 orbits
94.9	311	360	82.4	In orbit: classified payload
94.6	302	321	82.3	
88.2	111	124	95.4	Decayed 7-18-63: 100th Agena launched to date; classified payload
89.8	120	206	82.9	Decayed 8-13-63: classified payload
167.9	2274	2316	88.4	In orbit: classified payload
167.8	2290	2307	88.4	
167.9	2276	2319	88.4	In orbit: radiation pickaback returned data for 111 days
167.8	2289	2307	88.3	
168.0	2270	2326	88.4	In orbit: classified payload
167.9	2152	2450	88.4	

[1]Current orbital data as of March 1, 1964

Condensed Log of Space Projects (Cont.)

NAME	INT'L DESIG.	PROJECT DIRECTION	LAUNCH DATA			WEIGHT
			Date	Site	Vehicle	
Syncom 2	1963 31A	NASA	July 26, 1963	AMR	Delta	86
None	1963 32A	USAF	July 30, 1963	VAFB	Thor-Agena D	
Cosmos 19	1963 33A	USSR	Aug 6, 1963	Kapustin Yar		
None	1963 34A	USAF	Aug 24, 1963	VAFB	TAT-Agena D	
None None	1963 35A 1963 35B	USAF	Aug 29, 1963	VAFB	Thor-Agena D	
None	1963 36A	USAF	Sept 6, 1963	PA	Atlas-Agena D	
None	1963 37A	USAF	Sept 23, 1963	VAFB	TAT-Agena D	
None	None	USAF	Sept 27, 1963	PA	Scout	
None None	1963 38B 1963 38C	USAF/USN	Sept 28, 1963	VAFB	Thor-Able Star	160 120
None TRS 5 None	1963 39A 1963 39B 1963 39C	USAF	Oct 16, 1963	AMR	Atlas-Agena D	4.5
Cosmos 20	1963 40B	USSR	Oct 18, 1963	Tyuratum		
None None	1963 41A 1963 41B	USAF	Oct 25, 1963	PA	Atlas-Agena D	
None None	1963 42A 1963 42B	USAF	Oct 29, 1963	VAFB	TAT-Agena D	
Polyot 1	1963 43A	USSR	Nov 1, 1963			
None	None	USAF	Nov 9, 1963	VAFB	Thor-Agena D	
Cosmos 21	1963 44A	USSR	Nov 11, 1963	Tyuratam		
Cosmos 22	1963 45A	USSR	Nov 16, 1963	Tyuratam		
Explorer 18	1963 46 A	NASA	Nov 26, 1963	AMR	Delta	138
Atlas-Centaur 2	1963 47A	NASA	Nov 27, 1963	AMR	Atlas-Centaur	10,700
None	1963 48A	USAF	Nov 27, 1963	PA	Thor-Agena D	

ORBITAL DATA INITIAL/CURRENT[1]				RESULTS
Period	Perigee	Apogee	Incl.	
1454	22,062	22,750	33.1	In orbit: active-repeater synchronous comsat, moved to position over Brazil, communication tests successful, transmitting on 136, 1814 mc, to be moved to Pacific location
1437	22,239	22,246	32.8	
90.6	99	288	74.7	Decayed 8-11-63: classified payload
92.2	168	322	49.0	In orbit: unannounced payload
90.2	161	192	49.1	
89.5	104	202	75.0	Decayed 9-12-63: classified payload
90.8	183	202	81.9	Decayed 11-7-63: classified payload
92.0	195	262	81.9	Decayed 9-28-63: classified payload
				Decayed 9-13-63: classified payload
90.6	100	274	74.9	Decayed 10-12-63: classified payload
—	—	—	—	Failed to orbit: classified payload
107.4	676	714	89.9	In orbit: classified payload included 27-pound SNAP-9A nuclear power supply
107.3	670	698	89.9	
107.4	667	705	89.9	In orbit: classified payload, transmitting on 136.651 mc
107.3	670	698	89.9	
105 hrs	66,301	68,905	38.3	In orbit: classified payload
39 hrs	129	64,388	36.7	In orbit: radiation pickaback returned data for two weeks
				In orbit: classified payload
	123	186	65.0	Re-entered or decayed 10-30-63: unannounced payload
				Decayed 10-29-63: classified payload
				Decayed 10-29-63: classified payload
90.9	173	218	89.9	Decayed 1-21-64: classified payload
93.4	193	349	89.9	In orbit: classified payload
92.8	181	333	90.0	
	211	329		In orbit: first Soviet spacecraft with extensive maneuver capability
102.4	214	870	58.9	
—	—	—	—	Failed to orbit: classified payload
88.5	121	142	64.9	Re-entered or decayed 11-14-63: unannounced payload
90.3	127	245	64.9	Re-entered or decayed 11-22-63: unannounced payload
96.3 hrs	119	122,522	33.3	In orbit: IMP A, apogee lower than planned, transmitting on 136.110 mc, discovered high-energy radiation region beyond Van Allen belt
93.3 hrs	744	121,510	33.3	
107.7	303	1093	30.4	In orbit: AC-2 second stage, carried no experiments, not considered a spacecraft
107.9	297	1107	30.4	
90.1	109	236	70.0	Decayed 12-15-63: classified payload

[1]Current orbital data as of March 1, 1964

Condensed Log of Space Projects (Cont.)

NAME	INT'L DESIG.	PROJECT DIRECTION	LAUNCH DATA			WEIGHT
			Date	Site	Vehicle	
None	1963 49B	USAF/USN	Dec 5, 1963	VAFB	Thor-Able Star	
None	1963 49C					
Cosmos 23	1963 50A	USSR	Dec 13, 1963	Kapustin Yar		
None	1963 51A	USAF	Dec 18, 1963	PA	Atlas-Agena D	
Cosmos 24	1963 52A	USSR	Dec 19, 1963	Tyuratam		
Explorer 19	1963 53A	NASA	Dec 19, 1963	PA	Scout	15
None	None	USAF	Dec 20, 1963	VAFB	TAT-Agena D	
Tiros 8	1963 54A	NASA	Dec 21, 1963	AMR	Delta	265
None	1963 55A	USAF	Dec 21, 1963	VAFB	Thor-Agena D	
None	1963 55B					
None	1963 55C					
None	1964 1A	USAF/USN	Jan 11, 1964	VAFB	TAT-Agena D	
GGSE	1964 1B					
EGRS	1964 1C					
Greb 5	1964 1D					
None	1964 2A		Jan 19, 1964	VAFB	Thor-Agena D	
Relay 2	1964 3A	NASA	Jan 21, 1964	AMR	Delta	172
Echo 2	1964 4A	NASA	Jan 25, 1964	VAFB	Thor-Agena B	547
Saturn SA-5	1964 5A	NASA	Jan 29, 1964	AMR	Saturn I	37,700
Elektron 1	1964 6A	USSR	Jan 30, 1964			
Elektron 2	1964 6B					
Ranger 6	1964 7A	NASA	Jan 30, 1964	AMR	Atlas-Agena B	804
None	1964 8A	USAF	Feb 15, 1964	VAFB	TAT-Agena D	
None	1964 9A	USAF	Feb 25, 1964	PA	Atlas-Agena D	
Cosmos 25	1964 10A	USSR	Feb 27, 1964	Kapustin Yar		
None	1964 11A	USAF	Feb 27, 1964	PA	Atlas-Agena D	

| ORBITAL DATA INITIAL/CURRENT[1] | | | | RESULTS |
Period	Perigee	Apogee	Incl.	
107.2	665	690	90.0	In orbit: classified payload included SNAP-9A nuclear power
107.1	656	700	90.0	supply, transmitting on 150, 400 mc
107.2	666	689	90.0	In orbit: classified payload, transmitting on 54, 162, 324,
107.0	656	698	90.0	688 mc
92.9	149	381	49.0	In orbit: unannounced payload
90.8	137	255	49.0	
				Decayed 12-20-63: classified payload
90.5	131	254	65.0	Re-entered or decayed 12-24-63: unannounced payload
115.9	366	1487	78.6	In orbit: 12-foot balloon identical to Explorer 9, for atmospheric
115.8	368	1484	78.6	density studies
—	—	—	—	Failed to orbit: classified payload
99.3	430	473	58.5	In orbit: first Tiros to carry APT system, transmitting on
99.3	435	469	58.5	136.233, 136.924 mc
89.3	107	189	64.9	Decayed 1-9-64: classified payload
91.7	196	245	64.5	In orbit: classified payload
91.5	195	236	64.5	
				Status unknown: classified payload
103.5	563	578	69.9	In orbit: classified payload (initial orbital data as of 1-15-64)
103.4	564	579	69.9	
103.5	560	585	70.0	In orbit: gravity gradient stabilization experiment, transmitting
103.4	562	580	69.9	on 136.319 mc
103.5	563	578	69.9	
103.4	563	580	69.9	In orbit: classified payload, transmitting on 136.803 mc
103.5	563	578	69.9	
103.4	564	579	69.9	In orbit: solar radiation satellite transmitting on 136.886 mc
101.3	500	518	99.0	In orbit: classified payload (initial orbital data as of 1-31-64)
101.3	500	518	99.0	
194.7	1298	4606	46.0	In orbit: active-repeater comsat, transmitting on 136.140,
194.7	1302	4602	46.3	136.621 mc
108.8	642	816	81.5	In orbit: passive reflector comsat, first cooperative program
108.8	622	833	81.5	with USSR, beacon transmitting on 136.020, 136.170 mc
94.8	164	471	31.5	In orbit: Saturn I second stage (S-IV), carried no instruments,
94.7	163	465	31.5	not considered a spacecraft, transmissions on 136.995 mc
169	252	4412	61	In orbit: scientific satellite to study inner Van Allen radiation
169.3	245	4427	60.9	belt, first dual Soviet launch
1360	285	42,377	61	In orbit: identical to Elektron 1, intended to provide data on
1356.6	270	42,252	60.9	outer radiation belt
Flight time: 65.6 hours				Impacted on moon: closeup photographic experiment failed to provide data
				In orbit: classified payload
				Decayed 3-1-64: classified payload
92.3	169	316	49	In orbit: unannounced payload
92.4	161	326	49.1	
94.6	302	319	82.1	In orbit: classified payload

[1]Current orbital data as of March 1, 1964

Sounding Rockets

Perhaps man's first, tentative reaching of a finger into space comprised high-altitude rocket experiments made at White Sands Proving Grounds in New Mexico. Here, a tactical missile developed by the JPL for the Army and called the WAC Corporal was mounted piggyback on reconstructed German V-2 rockets and sent up higher into the sky than anyone had ever sent an earth-launched device before. Some of these sounding rockets, as they were called, carried cameras. Popular magazines carried pictures of the earth from 250 miles up in 1947 and 1948. These same sounding rockets took samples of the upper atmosphere, made limited measurements of cosmic-ray intensities, and counted other charged particles encountered above the earth's atmosphere.

Using techniques initially developed to tell scientists what was happening to a military rocket in flight, these first space venturers, the sounding rockets, telemetered back to the earth the readings of the instruments they carried with them. The sounding-rocket program is still being conducted, chiefly from Wallops Island in Virginia. This type of space vehicle, or spacecraft, is not intended to leave the earth's gravity, nor is it intended to go into orbit about the earth. The sounding-rocket program consists of a series of near-earth probes which go up from a few hundred to a few thousand miles above the surface of the earth, make a brief examination of their environment during the trip, and return to burn up in the earth's atmosphere or fall into the sea. This type of space traveler has not been included in the figures quoted above concerning comparison with Russia's launchings.

Earth Satellites

A second kind of man-made traveler in space is the earth satellite. Earth satellites are intended to go into orbit around the earth in such a way that their velocity of travel exactly balances the earth's gravitational pull so that they keep revolving about the earth in much the same way that the moon does. The orbits of these earth satellites are sometimes relatively circular, so that their distance from the earth is more or less constant at all times; however, they are usually elliptical, with the earth forming one of the foci of the ellipse. Thus the earth satellite comes close to the earth at one end of the oval path it follows, and then, having rounded the earth goes some distance out into space on the other half of its oval path only to return toward the earth once more. The orbits of earth satellites are usually expressed in terms of their perigee (the distance in miles of their closest approach to the earth) and apogee (distance in miles of their farthest excursion from the earth). For example, the Vanguard I satellite which was launched on March 17, 1958, was put into a 405/2,462-mile orbit; this means that at one end of its elliptical path it came within 405 miles of the earth and at the far end of its elliptical path it was 2,462 miles from the surface of the earth.

If space were truly a vacuum, and if the orbit of the satellite did not bring it even into the fringes of the earth's atmosphere (about 500 miles above the earth), there would be no reason for the satellite not to continue forever in the orbit in which it was placed by its rocket booster. However, the solar wind and sunlight itself exert pressure on the satellites as they travel their orbits about the earth. This pressure, of course, is most noticed when the satellite is traveling in a direction which is toward the sun. Vanguard I approaches its perigee (the nearest approach to earth) at the same time that it is approaching the sun; the result of these pressures on Vanguard I is to reduce its perigee by 1.2 miles per year, thus forcing it closer to the earth's atmosphere. The force of the solar wind, to be later reinforced by the drag of the earth's atmosphere, will eventually cause decay of this orbit and the destruction of Vanguard as it finally burns in a flaming descent into the earth's heavy atmosphere.

An earth satellite called Explorer VI, for example, was launched on August 7, 1959, into a 157/26,366-mile orbit. This highly elliptical orbit kept the satellite aloft until July of 1961, a period of almost two years in which the satellite, employing solar panels for power, transmitted the first crude TV photo of earth, recorded the presence of a large electrical current system encircling the earth, provided data for more detailed mapping of the Van Allen belts than had been previously possible, and brought new information on the earth's magnetic field and the presence of micrometeorites in space.

Most satellites are designed to accomplish a number of functions; nevertheless they usually have a prime function and by this they will be classified here. The several classes of satellites and their prime functions are as follows.

The scientific satellites are perhaps the most difficult to describe because they have so many functions, ranging from studies of what happens to certain materials in space, through interest in the earth's nearby (several thousand miles) environment, to the use of satellites as orbiting solar or planetary observatories outside the earth's atmosphere and hence beyond the limitations which that atmosphere imposes upon seeing our neighbors in the solar system. Most scientific satellites put in orbit to date have been labeled Explorer and given a number indicating which unit of this general class is being referred to.

Another class of satellites has been concerned with either passive or active communication of telephone, radio, scientific data, and television—both black and white and color—over long distances. It is hoped that some kind of a communication satellite system can be established which will permit direct and wireless transmission of such information around the world. The reason satellites are needed for this purpose is that the high frequencies—usually in the megacycle range—utilized for TV transmissions, for example, travel only in a straight line. Consequently, you cannot see a TV transmission beyond the horizon or, as they say, beyond the "line of sight." By use of communications satellites, a transmitter in New York could direct its transmitting beam to a satellite high in the heavens which could be seen both from New York and from Paris, with a receiving station at the latter location. The passive satellites have been named Echo, appropriately enough; while the active satellites have been named Telstar, Relay, and Syncom. The difference between the two is that in a passive satellite the transmitted signal is simply bounced off the satellite in the way that a tennis ball is bounced off a backboard. An active satellite, through its electronic circuitry, retransmits the signal, more like a tennis opponent firing the ball back at you with increased velocity. One of the most interesting active satellites is Syncom, and it differs from the other communications satellites presently being launched in that it is put into an earth orbit at such an altitude and at such a speed that it appears to remain stationary over a given point on the earth as the earth rotates. Three Syncom satellites spaced uniformly around the equator would make it possible to communicate with any place on the earth. A military communications satellite under the name of Courier has also received some tests.

Another interesting category of satellites comprises the meteorological or weather satellites with such names as Tiros and Nimbus. Tiros I, shaped something like a hatbox, was built by RCA for NASA and contained both narrow- and wide-angle television cameras and equipment for recording the cloud cover over the earth and transmitting pictures of it back to earth. Tiros was launched on April 1, 1960, and between then and June 17, 1960, it transmitted almost 23,000 pictures, of which approximately 60 per cent were useful.

Related to the weather satellites have been some military satellites of the "spy-in-the sky" type with such names as Midas and Samos. During 1961, the military were not so restrictive about the information on their spy satellites as they have become since that time. For example, it is public knowledge (TRW–STL *Space Log*) that Midas IV was launched from the Pacific Missile Range near Point Arguelo, California, in a 2,200-mile near-circular orbit over the poles on October 21, 1961. It reportedly detected a Titan missile launch from Cape Kennedy about 90 seconds after liftoff on October 26, 1961. Beginning in 1962, however, launches by the Army or the Air Force from Point Arguelo have been most frequently reported in the papers simply as follows: "The Air Force announced today from Vandenburg Air Force Base that a Thor Agena-B successfully placed an unidentified satellite in orbit."

Another very interesting use for satellites is to assist man in navigating the surface of the globe on which he lives. One big problem in navigating a trackless ocean, of course, is to figure out exactly where you are. The Navy hopes to simplify this problem through a series of satellites with which they have been experimenting under the class name of Transit. The Transit satellites, when perfected, are expected to broadcast their own position at a given point in time and space; the listening ship, or plane, can get a fix on the Transit satellite and, from the fix and the broadcast information about Transit's position, find its own position within a tenth of a mile.

The Air Force also has launched a number of satellites under the general title of Discoverer to experiment with recovery of capsules ejected from the satellites. The recovery may be made either after the capsules land in the sea or, in some cases, by actually snagging them in the air before they reach the surface of the water.

Then, of course, come the most interesting satellites of all, those that carry men in orbit around earth. On February 20, 1962, a Mercury satellite, lifted into orbit by an Atlas rocket booster, carried John Glenn into a 100/163-mile orbit. Glenn completed three circuits of the earth before splashing into the recovery area at sea, approximately 40 miles from the expected point, but only five miles from the destroyer *U.S.S. Noah*. Other astronauts have orbited the earth in Mercury satellites.

To follow the Mercury series is a series to be called Gemini, after the twins of Roman mythology. The Gemini spacecraft will carry two astronauts and will be lifted into space by the more powerful Saturn rocket, the Atlas not having sufficient thrust to lift the heavier Gemini spacecraft into orbit. The Saturn rocket is one of the first developed by the United States specifically for use in space exploration, the other boosters previously used having been military vehicles which were adapted for space purposes.

One of the most fascinating uses for satellites is that of earth-orbiting space stations where, in the future, will be assembled crews, supplies, and even the spacecraft for long interplanetary trips, such as out to Jupiter or Saturn. If future big rocket boosters can lift into orbit the crews, supplies, and powered spacecraft, the planet-bound voyage can start outside the earth's gravity, thus permitting the trip to be made in less time and with less power, since most of the present-day space voyagers' power is required simply to lift the spacecraft out of the earth's gravitational field.

As of this writing, space stations are satellites of the future.

Space Probes and Sun Satellites

Another category of man-made travelers in space are those intended to escape the earth's gravitational pull and journey to the moon, nearby planets, or toward the sun. Up to the present time, all spacecraft escaping the earth's gravitational pull have ended as satellites of the sun, whose gravitational pull they cannot escape with the power and techniques presently used.

There have been attempts by both Russia and the United States to place a satellite in orbit around the moon, but these attempts have been unsuccessful. The United States anticipates making a successful attempt of this type in connection with the project of placing men on the moon before the 1970's. The lunar-orbiting satellite is scheduled for some time in 1965.

The Russians have called their spacecraft sent to the vicinity of the moon, Lunik. The United States has two series of spacecraft for this purpose: one, called the Ranger, is intended to observe the lunar surface with television cameras and transmit the pictures back to earth; the other series, called the Surveyor, is intended to soft-land an instrument package on the moon to make a fairly detailed examination of the nature of the moon's surface and even of its structure as a preliminary to sending a manned spacecraft to the moon in the Apollo series. The Surveyor series of spacecraft is under construction by Hughes Aircraft Company for the JPL.

Another series of spacecraft, also developed at the JPL for the NASA, is called the Mariner. Spacecraft of this series are intended initially for fly-bys of some of our near neighbors in the solar system. The most spectacular of these, to date, has been Mariner II, which completed a 109-day, 180 million-mile trip to Venus on December 14, 1962, radioing back to earth the experiences of its trip and much new information on the nature of Venus itself. The latter information was acquired during a fly-by of 35 minutes as Mariner II passed Venus within 21,600 miles.

As with other spacecraft escaping the earth's gravitational field, after Mariner had passed Venus it went into orbit around the sun. As it was doing so, it continued to broadcast to earth its findings in space until January 3, 1963, some 20 days after it had completed its initial mission of scanning the clouds and surface of Venus.

Mariner established a number of records: (1) It transmitted usable information from the greatest distance in space up to the time of its trip, some 53 million miles away at the time it quit transmitting on January 3. (2) It was operational in space for the longest time of any spacecraft leaving the earth's gravitational field, 129 days. (3) It covered the most miles of any spacecraft in completing its mission by scanning Venus after a transit of 180 million miles through space. (The Russians launched a spacecraft toward Mars which would have exceeded some of these values if it had been successful, but it failed in its mission.)

The space ships of science fiction and the space comics have been portrayed as either highly streamlined projectiles or shaped like the Graf Zeppelin, with or without fins and exhaust ports for jet engines. In matter of fact, the satellites and the spacecraft which are in actual use today bear almost no resemblance to these streamlined devices of the comics writers' imaginations. Part of the reason is that, at the speeds we are using these devices in space today, the "aerodynamic drag" in the tenuous atmosphere of space is not a problem. The reason that a jet airplane, for example, is so streamlined is that it moves through the relatively dense atmosphere near the earth, and this streamlining helps it slip through the air more easily, with less drag than would be the case if it were round or square.

Recent studies, however, show that the plasma which makes up the sea of energy in interplanetary space reacts much the same in the presence of a rapidly moving body as does any other fluid, such as water or air. In fact, some earth satellites, such as Explorer VI, have sent back to earth information which enables scientists to draw a picture of the earth in its orbit through the plasma. This picture shows on the sunward side of the earth a typical, standing shock wave (just as though the earth were traveling rapidly toward the sun; instead, of course, it is the solar wind or plasma which is traveling rapidly from the sun toward the earth). Then there are the compressibility layers as the solar wind strikes the earth; and on the dark side of the earth is a long, teardrop-shaped cavity with turbulent edges, around which the particles of the solar wind attempt to resume their flow. (This is much like the "vacuum" behind a speeding plane or racing car, with turbulence along the edge of the vacuum before the particles which make up the air can resume their normal state after the passage of the high-speed object.) Consequently, as the speeds of our spacecraft increase we may find ourselves designing spacecraft in the streamlined form so favored by the science fiction writers. This will be particularly true if we are able to develop propulsion mechanisms which will thrust spacecraft toward the far planets and near stars at approximately the speed of light, as scientists even today dream of doing.

The Shape and Appearance of Spacecraft

In the meantime, however, when our satellites and spacecraft make most of their progress by the simple process of "falling" from one place to another at relatively low speeds, plasma drag and streamlining are not problems.

Under these conditions and because most of the power used in the spacecraft is to enable the device to escape (or reach an equilibrium with) earth's gravity, weight of the spacecraft has been an all-important factor. As a result, things are built as light as possible without much regard to their shape. The results are often weird and awe-inspiring.

Some spacecraft, of course, do have less startling shapes than others. The very first United States satellite, Explorer I, was shaped a lot like an oversized mechanical pencil with a rocket nozzle at the top (actually the bottom, as the device was launched, of course), and whiskers. The whiskers were four thin wires with weights at the ends used as a de-spin device; the spacecraft had been stabilized during launch by spinning it very rapidly (with its wire whiskers wrapped around its middle), but once it was in orbit it was desired to stop the spin. To accomplish this, a small explosive charge re-

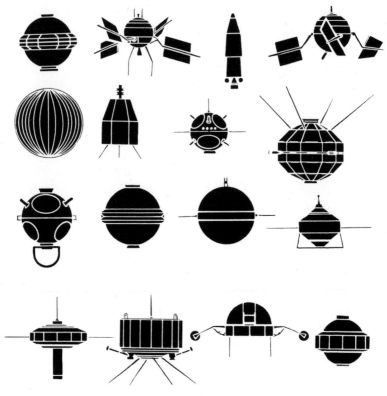

Variety of spacecraft shapes.

leased these long, weighted, wire whiskers so that they could unwrap from the body of the satellite, thus slowing its rotation to a stop in much the same manner that a spinning skater in the Ice Follies, with his arms close to his sides, brakes himself to a stop by letting his arms extend to their full length.

The Vanguard satellites of the International Geophysical Year were only slightly more exotic in appearance, each comprising a ball about as big as a good-sized grapefruit with certain unexplained bumps on it, plus six rodlike antennas extending out from it at different angles.

Pioneer II was not so startling either, though a complete departure from the previous two in that it looked like a very thick disk with a bowl upended on each side. From the bottom of one bowl extended a rocket nozzle and from the bottom of the other extended a number of knobs and antennas.

Things got more interesting, in appearance at least, when the scientists began to use solar panels to supplement batteries as power sources for the radios and other instruments in the satellites. Solar panels on these early spacecraft extend out from the craft like big paddles, thin as possible, of course, to conserve weight, and covering as big an area as possible to gather as much sunlight as possible. Explorer VI, which was put into a 157/26,366-mile orbit on August 7, 1959, was essentially a big ball with four solar panels extended out from it on brackets at predetermined, but awkward-looking, angles. Pioneer V, launched into interplanetary space on March 11, 1960, was of this same general design; it wound up as a satellite of the sun.

The Tiros series of weather satellites looked like nothing so much as a big hatbox with a rod antenna extending out the top and a TV-camera lens extending out the bottom. Discoverer XIII, first manmade object to be recovered from orbit by the Air Force, could have been mistaken for the tub out of a Maytag washer with a couple of knobs and bumps on the lid.

The Courier 1-B, army communications satellite, was designed as a 51-inch sphere, the surface of which was covered with solar cells, thus eliminating the necessity for the odd-shaped paddles; but, of course, the function of this satellite made this structure possible, while some of the other spacecraft needed other instruments on the surface which could not function if they were covered by solar cells.

Other spacecraft look like such things as a dunce cap with spikes around the headband and a ball on the tip, a four-layer wedding cake, a wedge-shaped "chunk" of material, and a small pyramid pierced by an arrow (the antenna). One of the strangest of all was perhaps the Mariner II spacecraft, which greatly resembled an arthritic dragonfly with a miniature model of the Eiffel tower on its head. The dragonfly's wings, of course, were the inevitable solar panels; the Eiffel tower was an aluminum structure containing instruments necessary to conduct the experiments planned for the trip and to observe Venus at the time of fly-by.

The Harsh Environment of Space

One of the most difficult problems in designing spacecraft is to protect the instruments and the "works" from overheating once the spacecraft gets out into space. We are all familiar with how hot an object, particularly a metal object and especially a black metal object, gets when left out in the sun on a summer day on earth. Even a clay road, which reflects much of the sunlight falling upon it (instead of absorbing it and holding it as heat) gets so hot in the summer sun that it is agony to walk barefoot on it. The common phenomena just described occur on earth, where we are shielded by the thick, friendly blanket of atmosphere between us and the sun. This same atmosphere protects us from the direct rays of the sun and flows constantly over the earth, moving heat from hot places to cool and bringing cool breezes to ameliorate the strongest rays of the sun where they fall most fiercely on the earth.

Out in the harsh environment of space there is no atmosphere to shield the spacecraft from the direct rays of the sun; furthermore, in some cases, such as the Mariner II trip to Venus, the spacecraft gets closer and closer to the sun as the trip continues.

As the spacecraft approaches the sun, the intensity of the sun's light and heat becomes greater in, as the scientists say, inverse proportion to the square of the distance from the sun. This means that if you halve the distance to the sun, the intensity of the light and heat is multiplied by four; if you cut the distance to the sun to one-third, the light and heat are nine times as great.

Because of the problems of heat (and cold) in the harsh environment of space, spacecraft are often painted in startling and irregu-

Mariner II spacecraft as it appeared in flight to Venus. (*Jet Propulsion Laboratory*)

lar patterns of gold, silver, white, and black. It is the intention of the designers to keep those areas painted in the light colors as cool as possible, by virtue of the fact that light colors reflect the sun's heat away from the spacecraft. On the other hand, areas needing solar heat are painted dark colors so that they will absorb the sun's rays. Actual gold leaf and silver plating are used in some spacecraft designs, because their reflection characteristics—therefore their ability to keep the area cool—are even greater than those of white paint. Each of these substances has a certain characteristic reflectivity—i.e., it reflects a certain percentage of the light and heat falling upon it. Knowing these values, spacecraft designers use the substance that will keep the part of the spacecraft they are interested in as near as possible to the temperature it should be.

Because spacecraft often change position in relation to the sun, as does a satellite circling the earth, great care must be taken in the design of the spacecraft and in the arrangement of its parts so that a reflecting surface intended to keep a certain portion of the spacecraft cool will not reflect the sun's light directly onto another part of the spacecraft which would thus become overheated. Anyone who has experimented with signaling with a mirror on a sunny day knows that this problem of determining where the reflected light will fall in a rotating or otherwise maneuvering spacecraft is no simple one.

The great cold of interplanetary space poses other serious problems for spacecraft designers. Under the near-absolute-zero conditions of interplanetary space (for those parts shaded from the sun), rubber and plastics become more brittle than glass, and metals lose their tensile and bending strengths.

The very vacuum of space causes further strange things to happen: in earth atmosphere a door hinge works, in part, because the molecules of air between the pin and the hinge act as a sort of lubricant to keep the metal surfaces apart and let them turn freely over each other. In the near vacuum of space this "lubricating" feature of the atmosphere is absent; metals in contact with each other for any length of time occasionally fuse as if they were one piece of metal, their molecules intermingling so intimately that there is no space between them and the hinge will not work. Ordinary lubricants, such as oil, either "freeze" in the deep cold, or evaporate in the vacuum of space.

These problems are by no means completely solved as yet, but at least the engineers who design the spacecraft are now aware of many difficulties which they did not even suspect before they began putting satellites and other spacecraft into orbit. This is the most important reason why "debugging" spacecraft on the ground, before flight, can never be completely successful—there are always conditions encountered in space of which we know nothing on earth. The only way to learn about them is to fly the craft and see what happens.

Launching spacecraft to find out what happens to them, while it is the most effective method, is also quite expensive. Consequently, scientists are building space simulation chambers on earth in which they hope to *approach* the conditions in space closely enough so that they can get an idea what is going to happen. As indicated early in this book, the vacuum in space is approximately one million times as good as any vacuum so far achieved in a laboratory on earth; this means that, at least for a long time, man will not be able to *duplicate* the vacuum of space on earth. Consequently, he cannot tell *exactly* what will happen to the spacecraft in space; but, as his laboratory vacuum approaches that in space, he can get an idea of what will happen. This same general principle applies to other attempts to simulate space conditions in earth laboratories—we can only approach the conditions of space, but so far have not been able to duplicate them. Therefore, while we can get some idea of what may happen to our devices when they leave the earth's atmosphere, we can never be sure until we actually launch them.

3. Astrogation

Navigating in space, or "astrogation," if we may call it that, is quite a bit more difficult than navigating on earth for a number of reasons.

Earth navigation is difficult enough. Imagine yourself, for example, in the middle of the Pacific Ocean at a point where the water extends to the horizon in all directions and there is nothing but tossing billows for a thousand or more miles in whatever direction you look. Your chief problem, of course, is to find out where *you* are. The earth's surface has been mapped, and if you can find out where you are in the ocean, you can mark your position on the map. Then, with the sun, a compass, or some other direction-finding device you direct your ship toward the port that you would like to reach, say San Francisco. Finding out where you are on the rolling oceans is done with an instrument called a sextant, which takes sights upon, of all things, the stars!

With the sextant, by measuring the angles to two or more known stars, you can find your location on the surface of the sea. Then, because the continents of the earth are fixed in their relationship to each other, you can—with a compass—proceed confidently toward the port of your desire.

Navigation in space, on the other hand, is quite a different matter! The "place where you are," the earth, is not a fixed place in space— it is moving around the sun at about eighteen and a half miles a second, or 68,000 miles an hour. The sun, itself, about which the earth moves, carries the earth along with it on the sun's path in the great spinning wheel of the galaxy at about twelve miles a second. And, of course, the earth is rotating on its axis at about 1,000 miles an hour so that the platform from which the space vehicle is launched has three different high-speed motions at the instant of launch, and elements of all three of these motions are imparted to the spacecraft at the instant it leaves the pad. In addition, the "harbor" toward which the spacecraft is navigating has its own kinds of motions at speeds of thousands of miles per hour. To conserve travel time and distance, the spacecraft is "aimed" at where the target planet is going to be by the time the spacecraft gets there, rather than pointed directly at the planet it is desired to intercept.

. . . 3, 2, 1, Zero, Fire!

For example, launching Mariner II toward Venus has been likened to the difficulty of shooting at a dime at a distance of 200 yards from a seat on a merry-go-round mounted on a truck tearing down a highway, while the dime itself was mounted on a truck on a roughly parallel road and moving at a greater speed.

In addition to the difficulties occasioned by the fact that both your starting place and your destination are in several kinds of motion simultaneously, at speeds of many miles per second, there is another complication in astrogation which is not usually encountered in navigation on earth. This is the fact that spacecraft, up to this time, are really not powered while they are moving from one place to another— they are coasting! Or falling, if you prefer this term.

The tremendous thrust of booster rockets, with their spectacular bursts of flame and awesome, ear-splitting thunder, only act to lift the spacecraft out of the earth's field of gravitation, or bring it into balance with the earth's field of gravitation in the case of satellites which orbit the earth. Thus, after a few seconds of powered flight during which the spacecraft becomes free of Earth gravity, the spacecraft simply "falls" toward the planet aimed at. In the case of a satellite, of course, the spacecraft continually falls away from the earth and is continually pulled back by the earth's gravity so that the satellite achieves a circular or elliptical orbit around the earth.

In the case of a spacecraft journeying to another planet the problem might be likened (except for the fact that the relative distances are much greater than on earth) to a person who pushed off from a dock in Tokyo with his foot impelling his rowboat in the general direction of San Francisco, and then (without oars or other means of propulsion) sat down on the thwarts to await his arrival in San Francisco, subject to the buffeting of winds and currents and depending on the attraction of the west coast metropolis to draw him to its harbor.

It is easy to imagine that under these conditions you might not push off exactly in the direction of San Francisco, and taking into account all the forces which would act on the rowboat during the transit, it is easy to imagine also that you might never arrive there!

If, in addition, San Francisco itself were moving rapidly about the earth's surface during the transit of the rowboat, then the problem would be comparable to that encountered in launching a spacecraft to, say, Venus or Mars.

There is one big advantage the spacecraft launchers do have and this is that the *major* forces at work on their spacecraft in its transit from planet to planet are more predictable and are more subject to the laws of mathematics than is, for example, the Japanese Current in the illustration we just gave of the trip from Tokyo to San Francisco. Thus, we know and can predict mathematically the influence of the earth's gravity on the "fall" of the spacecraft between here and Venus. In the same way we can predict the effects on its course of the gravitational pull of the sun, of Venus, of the moon, of Mars, of other planets of the solar system; and all these elements do have an influence on the course or trajectory, as it is called, of the spacecraft in its transit from earth to Venus.

In a similar way the pressure of sunlight on a spacecraft is predictable enough that it can be taken into account in directing the spacecraft toward Venus. On the other hand, the solar wind, which is gusty and sometimes intense, at other times slow and not very dense, cannot be predicted in its short-term variations any more than the wind at sea can be predicted exactly in terms of its direction and intensity during the rowboat trip from Tokyo to San Francisco.

All of the factors influencing a spacecraft trajectory must be known for the *instant* of its launch, and their effects on its course be calculated almost instantaneously, so that the spacecraft may be aimed in the right direction at the instant of blastoff. This is one of the great problems about spacecraft launching countdowns: if the spacecraft cannot be launched at the instant planned, then all of the complicated mathematical equations have to be refigured for the new instant of launch because the rotational position and orbital location of the earth are constantly changing, as are the location of the target planet and as are the interrelationships of all the gravitational fields of the sun and its planets. It is easy to see that without modern high-speed computers it would be impossible to launch a spacecraft with any accuracy at all, because the simple mass of mathematical calculation necessary to feed right commands into the launching rocket's guidance system would take many man-years of time to complete. Even the computers cannot do this job instantaneously, so most countdowns have predetermined "holds" built into them to allow for minor repairs to be made to elements of the spacecraft or its booster if either is found to be malfunctioning. By thus allowing time for minor repairs in the scheduled countdown, it is hoped in most cases that the spacecraft will be lifted off the pad at the instant originally planned even if some minor troubles have developed during the countdown.

If the planned launching time is missed by only a small amount, a computer on standby can keep reworking the "fine adjustments" of the necessary launching equations continuously so that no real delay need be encountered; but if any substantial delay occurs, some of the basic equations might have to be changed in such a way that the computer may require several hours or even days to recalculate the trajectory.

Further, because the planets are changing position in relation to each other all the time, and because our present boosters are limited in the escape speed that they can impart to a spacecraft leaving our gravitational field, there are only certain occasions in the dance of the planets when they approach each other closely enough or are in the right relationship to each other for a spacecraft to get from earth to one of the other planets. These critical periods of time in which a successful launch can be accomplished are called launching "windows."

A spacecraft leaving the earth either for the moon or for one of the planets must have a velocity of at least seven miles per second (roughly 25,000 miles per hour) in order to leave the earth's field of gravity, as we say. Actually, this is not the true case, because—as was described above—the gravitational fields of the sun, earth, moon, planets, and nearby stars are always acting upon a spacecraft within the solar system, but in greater or lesser degree. What we really mean when we say that a spacecraft escapes the earth's field of gravity is that we propel it fast enough to reach a point between our planet and its objective where the field of gravity of the objective becomes stronger than the field of gravity of the earth and therefore pulls the spacecraft toward the objective.

Thus, as a spacecraft leaves the earth at 25,000 miles an hour it is still being pulled back toward the earth by the earth's force of gravity and consequently loses speed relative to the earth. The spacecraft which leaves the earth's ionosphere at a speed of around 25,000 miles an hour on a trip to the moon will slow down to less than 4,000 miles an hour as it approaches the moon because the pull of the earth's gravity is the stronger until the spacecraft has traversed about five-sixths of the distance between the earth and the moon. At this point the gravitational field of the earth has become so weak that the relatively weak gravity of the moon is stronger, so the moon begins to attract the spacecraft, which begins to "fall" toward the moon with increasing velocity.

The same general situation, but with a more complicated pattern of speedups and slowdowns due to the several gravitational fields affecting it, is experienced by a spacecraft on the way to Mars or Venus.

You Can't Get There from Here!

For simplicity, it has been made to sound as though there were no control at all over the spacecraft once its booster engines cut off and it was in free flight toward its objective. This is not literally true. The Mariner II spacecraft for Venus, for example, was made to conduct a very complicated "mid-course maneuver" about nine days after it had left the earth, when earth observation of its trajectory had become precise enough, and the computers had had time enough to determine by exactly how much it was going to miss Venus. The miss distance calculated by the computers at this time was believed to be about 230,000 miles.

This is not a bad miss in a total trip of 180 million miles—only about ⅛ of 1 per cent. Nevertheless, a 230,000-mile miss would have put Mariner instruments beyond their effective range for examining Venus. Consequently, a command was send from earth which caused the Mariner spacecraft to turn off its cruising-type scientific experiments (so that the power would be available for the following maneuver), turn itself around so that it was pointing toward the earth (although still moving toward Venus), and fire briefly, for a very carefully measured few seconds and fraction of a second, a retrorocket of a very carefully calculated power. This maneuver resulted in "slowing down" the Mariner in relation to Venus, because the 230,000-mile miss was going to be occasioned by the spacecraft reaching the point of intended Venus intercept before Venus did.

This slowdown maneuver was so carefully calculated that it changed the miss distance from 230,000 miles to 21,600 miles, thus bringing the Mariner instruments, which could work effectively between 8,000 and 40,000 miles from the planet, within working range of Venus 100 days later.

Once this slowdown maneuver had been completed, the spacecraft turned itself around once more so that its instruments were pointed in the right direction, resumed operating these instruments, and went serenely on its way toward its rendezvous with the morning star.

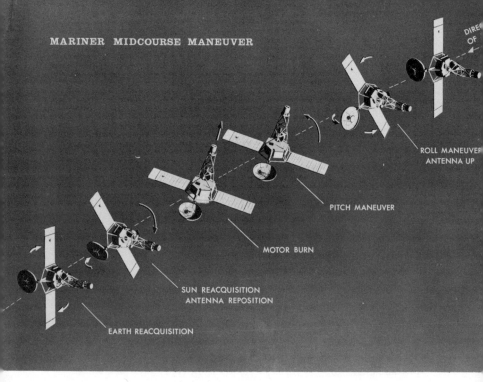

DIRE
OF

ROLL MANEUVER
ANTENNA UP

PITCH MANEUVER

MOTOR BURN

SUN REACQUISITION
ANTENNA REPOSITION

EARTH REACQUISITION

Mariner II midcourse maneuver conducted on the way to Venus to refine its flight path for observation of Venus. (*Jet Propulsion Laboratory*)

Rendezvous in Space

Another kind of control of the spacecraft that can be exercised when it is in flight is called attitude control. The attitude control mechanism is the one which enabled Mariner to turn around on command before firing its retrorocket and then to reorient itself in the proper direction after the retrorocket action had been completed. But attitude control can be used advantageously for finer adjustments of attitude, as well.

When a spacecraft is put in free flight by a rocket booster, it is usually undesirable for the shell of the booster to accompany the spacecraft, so they are separated by small explosive charges built into the joint between the spacecraft and its booster. It is not always possible to insure that each of these several small explosive charges will exert exactly the same force when they separate the spacecraft and its booster. The result of this fact, plus vibrations set up by the launching process itself, often cause a spacecraft to tumble in orbit. Tumbling means turning end over end or from side to side as the spacecraft progresses along its trajectory.

Many of the experiments which spacecraft are intended to perform, and certainly communication with the spacecraft over the great distances encountered and with the low power used, require that the spacecraft remain oriented in a proper attitude as it makes its trip, thus keeping instruments pointed in the right direction and keeping antennas pointed directly at the earth for maximum efficiency. This attitude control is accomplished by a number of little nozzles in the spacecraft which are usually served by a common pressure vessel containing a gas (often nitrogen) under great pressure. These nozzles are usually arranged around what are called the three axes of rotation: the long axis, or the axis that is pointing in the direction of travel; the horizontal axis, intersecting the first at right angles and about which the spacecraft might wobble up and down, or "pitch;" and the vertical axis, intersecting the other two and about which the spacecraft might wobble from left to right, or "yaw." There are inertial sensors aboard the spacecraft (in principle, like small pendulums) which can detect any pitch or yaw of the spacecraft and automatically trigger emission of a little jet of nitrogen from the proper nozzle to stop the undesired motion and keep the spacecraft in the proper attitude.

It is this kind of attitude control which is built into the Mercury spacecraft which carry our astronauts around the earth, too. The attitude control devices in these spacecraft can be fully automatic or, at the option of the astronaut, can be brought under his manual control so that he can "fly" the spacecraft himself without interference from the automatic control. This manual feature allows him to turn the spacecraft in any direction he desires so that he can look to his left, right, or even behind him, as well as in the direction in which he is traveling.

As our manned space flight activities become more complicated this manual control of spacecraft attitude will be enlarged to permit the joining, or "docking," of two spacecraft in flight. This will permit two astronauts or groups of astronauts sent up in separate spacecraft to rendezvous at some chosen place in space after they are in orbit around the earth or even on a trajectory toward another planet.

This capability will require a great deal of skill and practice and —certainly for the first few trials—will involve great dangers, but it will increase our capacity to maneuver spacecraft in useful ways.

Advances in attitude control, plus use of secondary-power rockets (similar to Mariner's retrorocket) will be used to put the Apollo three-man spacecraft into orbit around the moon. The effect will be to provide partially powered flight (instead of free "fall") to the moon. Once in orbit around the moon the Apollo will send a rocket-powered lunar excursion module (LEM), containing two men, to the surface of the moon while the remaining astronaut continues to orbit the moon in the Apollo. Upon completing the excursion upon the surface of the moon the LEM will rejoin the Apollo in lunar orbit so that the men can enter its command module for the return journey to earth.

4. Communication and Tracking

The coming of the space age certainly changed the scope and the nature of electronic communication, affecting both radio and radar. It gave the able and ambitious young practitioners of this relatively new art literally new worlds to conquer. Radio transmission used to be thought of in extreme distances of several thousand miles, and then in terms of a single or multiple bounce off the ionospheric layers in the earth's upper atmosphere so that "line of sight" transmission could reach points beyond the horizon. With the coming of the space age, the sky was literally the limit. If you could see as far as the moon, the challenge was to send a radio signal that far. Radar practitioners began bouncing signals off the moon.

Not only was a tremendous challenge here and an almost unlimited field of action, but the space age put great demands upon radio and radar communication in its need for getting information back from spacecraft in space.

Electronic Robots

A highly instrumented spacecraft, in the present state of the art, is simply a mechanical and electronic messenger, with greater or less complication and more or less built-in intelligence. Man is sending these out into space to places where he cannot yet go in the hope that this robot messenger will send back to earth information about con-

85

ditions in space which may enable man to build spacecraft in which he himself can journey to these far places one day.

If this electronic-brain messenger being sent into space is going to complete successfully its mission, it must send back information about its experiences and discoveries in space. The messenger must also be capable of receiving and acting upon commands transmitted from earth. The scientists who construct these spacecraft messengers usually provide for several alternate courses of action from which they can select in the light of the spacecraft's experience in space. Thus, when the spacecraft returns information about what is going on in space, men on earth may make decisions about the spacecraft's next action, course of its trajectory, attitude toward the sun or other stars or planets, or what experiment should be tried next. Once these decisions, based upon information supplied by the spacecraft, have been made, then the decision must be transmitted back to the spacecraft to command it to take whatever action its controllers on earth deem advisable.

This need for rapid and complex two-way communication over vast distances has been a challenge to the electronic engineers, one which they have met with a flair!

The challenge has been not only one of tremendous distances— millions of miles in space versus a few hundred or two or three thousand on earth—but also one of miniaturization and low power. Both space and weight are at a premium on a spacecraft; consequently all instruments, including radio and telemetry transceivers are miniaturized and subminiaturized to get the utmost in performance out of a few ounces of weight and fractions of cubic inches of space.

Power is another problem. The average big-city commercial radio station has a power output of approximately 50,000 watts. Because of the limitations of using solar panels for power, many spacecraft operate all their instruments, including their radio and telemetry transponders, on a total power of perhaps 3½ watts.

It is easy to send a strong signal from earth to the spacecraft, because the earth transmitter can be built as big and as powerful as desired. When the spacecraft speaks to earth, however, the power output from say 50 million miles away may be as low as 1½ watts, which was the case with the spacecraft Mariner II which made the first visit to the environment of Venus in December 1962.

Deep-Space Tracking Net

The world-wide tracking and communication networks which make these incredible feats of communication possible have, as their title suggests, two major functions. The first is to track the spacecraft very accurately so that men on earth may know whether it is following the course prescribed for it and, if not, can take whatever action is available to correct the spacecraft's performance and bring it near to the prescribed course.

The second function is to receive from the spacecraft the tremendous outpouring of information from scientific instruments and engineering devices which monitor the spacecraft's own performance; this information is sent back to earth by the spacecraft under the guidance of an electronic brain aboard the spacecraft in a form called telemetry.

Let us consider for a few moments the world-wide tracking and communication network conceived and constructed for NASA by the JPL—a network called the Deep-Space Instrumentation Facility (DSIF).

The DSIF has three major locations almost equally spaced around the world, at approximately 120° of longitude from each other. These are at Johannesburg, South Africa; at Woomera, Australia (with a supporting facility at Canberra); and in the Mojave Desert at Goldstone, California, which is the headquarters location for the net, reporting directly to the JPL.

The Goldstone complex comprises three tracking sites called Pioneer (DSIF-2), Echo (DSIF-3), and Venus.

The Pioneer site has an 85-foot diameter parabolic antenna which can be pointed with an accuracy better than 0.02° of arc. This antenna has an hour-angle axis parallel to the polar axis of the earth, and a declination axis which is perpendicular to the polar axis and

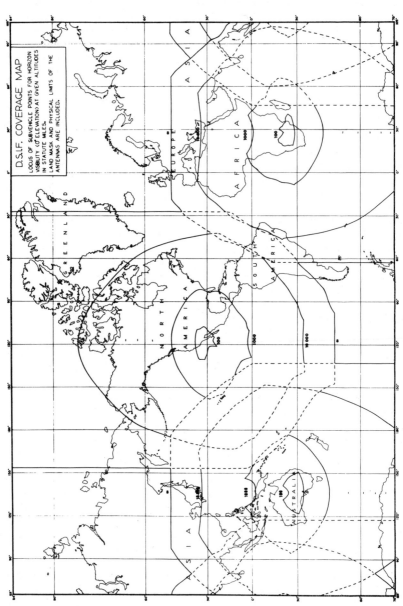

Map showing how three DSIF stations provide around-the-world coverage of a spacecraft flight to the moon or planets. *(Jet Propulsion Laboratory)*

parallel to the equatorial plane of the earth. This kind of mounting is called a "polar mount," and permits tracking by moving the antenna about only one axis. The antenna weighs approximately 240 tons and has a maximum rotation rate of approximately 1° per second, and a minimum rate of 0.00418° per second, which is equal to the rotation rate of the earth. This antenna, and all other large "dishes" in the DSIF are driven by two electric motors working through a hydraulic mechanism; the two motors work simultaneously in the same direction but at different speeds, so that one is always pushing the antenna while the other one, in effect, is dragging its heels. This arrangement means that the gears of the second motor and its drive are always in position to reverse the direction of the antenna without any backlash; the motor which has been leading then follows.

The antenna of Goldstone's Pioneer site has a Cassegrain feed system that is very similar to the type used in large reflector telescopes: a convex cone at the center of the main dish gathers the signal in conjunction with the main dish itself and reflects the signal to a sub-reflector at the focus of the parabolic curve where the energy is concentrated in a narrow beam and reflected back to the feed collector point near the center of the main dish. This type of feed system minimizes the noise inherent in the antenna itself by reducing interference from radio energy received by the back of the dish. It also permits a more convenient location of the various feed components This antenna at the Pioneer site of the Goldstone complex is equipped with an extremely sensitive, low-noise, combination of a maser and a parametric amplifier. (*Maser* is an acronym for *m*icrowave *a*mplification through *s*timulated *e*mission of *r*adiation.) The parametric amplifier is "pumped" or excited by microwave energy from the maser in such a way that the amplitude of the incoming desired signal is augmented, in relation to the receiving system's own electronic noise, to such a degree that a weak spacecraft signal can be detected and "read" at a distance twice as far as would be possible without this feature. The same capability improves the tracking effectiveness of the installation.

Additional details of the Goldstone Pioneer site, together with

The DSIF tracking and command complex at Goldstone, California. (*Jet Propulsion Laboratory*)

information on the Echo and Venus sites and the Woomera and Johannesburg stations are shown in Table 3.

TABLE 3

STATIONS OF THE DEEP-SPACE INSTRUMENTATION FACILITY (DSIF)

Location	Station	Equipment	Function
Between launch site and first downrange permanent station	DSIF 1 Mobile Tracking Stations	Antenna: 10-foot Transceiver: 25 watt, 890-Mc	Fast scan, early acquisition of spacecraft, as a "bird dog" for nearest permanent station
Johannesburg, South Africa	DSIF 5	Antenna: 85-foot polar mount, Cassegrain feed Receiver: parametric amplifier Transmitter: 10-kw, 890-Mc	Reception of telemetry Tracking of spacecraft Transmission of commands For all East-launched spacecraft this is the first permanent station to pick them up
Woomera, Australia	DSIF 4	Antenna: 85-foot, polar mount Receiver: parametric amplifier	Reception of telemetry Tracking of spacecraft
Goldstone, California	Pioneer Site DSIF 2	Antenna: 85-foot, polar mount, Cassegrain feed Receiver: master and parametric amplifier	Reception of telemetry Tracking of spacecraft
	Echo Site DSIF 3	Antenna: 85-foot, polar mount Receiver: parametric amplifier Transmitter: 10-kw, 890-MC	Transmission of commands Tracking of spacecraft Standby reception of telemetry
	Venus Site	Antenna: 85-foot radar-type	Advanced radar astronomy investigations Communications research

The sensitivity of these receivers is such that they can detect radio-frequency energy proportionately equal to that radiated by a 1-watt light bulb at a distance of 75 to 80 million miles. The energy from such a source, as received at the antenna, would be a 20 sextillionth of a watt (0.00000000000000000002 or 2×10^{-20}).

Closeup of the Cassegrain feed on a tracking antenna. (*Jet Propulsion Laboratory*)

The output of the Mariner spacecraft as it passed Venus was of the order of 3 watts, and the distance was only about 39 million miles. Consequently, the energy received at the antenna on this occasion was 0.000000000000000001 or 1×10^{-18} watt. A perfectly efficient storage battery charged at this rate for 30 billion years would accumulate enough energy to light an ordinary 1-watt flashlight bulb for approximately one second.

If the Mariner II spacecraft had continued to function as it went into orbit about the sun, and continued to point its directional antenna at the earth, useful information could have been received by the DSIF stations out to a distance of 150 to 200 million miles; the spacecraft could have been tracked by these same stations to 300 or 400 million miles.

Since most spacecraft (of a nonmilitary nature) are being launched from Cape Kennedy, and because they are usually launched toward the east in order to take advantage of the 1,000-mile per hour rotation rate of the earth in giving them a good start on their journey, the first DSIF station to pick up a newly launched spacecraft is the one in Johannesburg, South Africa.

However, supplementing the permanent stations are two mobile fast-scan tracking outfits, one of which is normally used near the Cape to check the performance of the booster and spacecraft immediately following liftoff. The second mobile station is usually located in South Africa up-course from the Johannesburg station, and this mobile facility helps the big "dish" at Johannesburg find and "lock on" the spacecraft in the early stages of its flight.

Both mobile facilities are contained in vans so that they may be moved to advantageous locations. Both are capable of a higher tracking rate than the fixed stations, because during that part of the spacecraft flight in which they are used the spacecraft is relatively close to the earth and therefore appears to move across the sky more rapidly than it will when it has progressed farther away from the earth on its journey. These small, agile, mobile stations pick up a spacecraft, get a quick "fix" on its trajectory, and relay the information to the bigger, permanent station they support so that it can direct its antenna into tracking position with a minimum of lost time and motion. The Johannesburg station, also kown as DSIF 5, has an 85-foot, polar-mount antenna with a parametric amplifier similar to that of the Echo site at Goldstone. The function of DSIF-5 is the reception of information telemetered from spacecraft, the tracking of a spacecraft during the time of the earth's rotation when the spacecraft is "in view" from this site, and the transmission of commands to the spacecraft under the same conditions. Its transmitter has a power of 10 kilowatts and it operates on a frequency of 890 megacycles.

Normally, the next station to pick up a spacecraft after launch is that at Woomera, Australia. However, because of the rotation of the earth, Woomera first sights a planet-bound spacecraft in the east: the rotation of the earth makes the spacecraft *appear* to "turn back" from Johannesburg and disappear over its western horizon at approximately the same time that it appears or "rises" over the eastern horizon for Woomera, Australia. From this point on, as the earth rotates under the traveling spacecraft, the tracking network observes the spacecraft in a manner similar to that for any heavenly body rising in the east and setting in the west.

Most earth-orbiting satellites launched in the same west-to-east manner, because they remain relatively close to the earth, would be detected by all tracking stations "rising" in the west. They cross the sky from west to east and "set" below the eastern horizon.

At Woomera, Australia, an 85-foot, polar-mounted antenna with the now familiar parametric amplifier tracks the spacecraft and receives telemetered information. This facility is not equipped to issue commands to the spacecraft.

Space Flight Operations Center

All of the sites and facilities are connected to the Space Flight Operations Center (SFOC) at the JPL in Pasadena, California, by duplicate radio teletype and radio telephone facilities—duplicate so that if one communication link should fail during a critical period in the flight of the spacecraft the other would be available for communicating necessary information.

The SFOC includes, of course, a communications center to monitor the network's communication circuits and to accept and transmit information. The communications center is closely associated with a central computing facility where, again, the electronic brains are busy almost continuously during a flight, accepting, digesting, manipulating, and displaying data acquired from the spacecraft so that its earthbound monitors can tell what is happening to it and decide what it should be commanded to do.

During the many days and nights required for the spacecraft to reach its objective the communications center is one of the busiest areas. The teletype and radio links from the Cape, the mobile stations, as well as South Africa, Australia, and the headquarters tracking facility at Goldstone, all feed into the center. In addition, from Goldstone a high-speed data line bypasses the communications center and links directly with the central computing facility for quick, real-time (concurrent with the event) processing of essential flight and tracking information.

From the communications center, both teletype data and voice circuits are connected to the various offices and control rooms within the JPL where the mission-control activities are centered, and where the telemetered data from the spacecraft are continually studied.

In the SFOC, the technical and scientific advisory panels continually report to the mission manager performance of the spacecraft in flight, comparisons of the real trajectory of the spacecraft with the planned trajectory, and a continuous series of commands (from data calculated by the computers) required for trajectory correction at any point during the mission. In addition, of course, the teams which are monitoring the telemetered reports of the scientific experiments contained in the spacecraft are feeding in their reports to the SFOC also. Usually this effort is organized on a team basis, with teams for spacecraft data analysis, scientific data analysis, orbit determination, tracking data analysis, and trajectory correction commands.

The SFOC is equipped with boards depicting the portion of the heavens through which the spacecraft will go and on which its course is traced by means of glowing lights, illuminated as the spacecraft makes progress toward its objective. In addition to the trajectory information and data regarding the progress of the spacecraft along this trajectory, other displays show temperature and pressure readings, and summaries of data telemetered from the spacecraft scientific experiments or engineering-monitoring subsystems.

The Space Flight Operations Center, cutaway illustration showing flight displays, control positions, and some of the electronic brains for analyzing flight data. (*Jet Propulsion Laboratory*)

Within the SFOC closed-circuit television is used to coordinate the activities of the various teams taking part in the mission control operation. Under the control of the mission manager, the test director, or the DSIF operations manager, the entire operations room can be kept under surveillance, using cameras controlled in pan, tilt, and zoom. In addition, six fixed cameras continually view teletype printers and display the printout on television monitors in four consoles.

Electronic Brains

The modern electronic computer is not only important during the countdown and launching of a spacecraft, but is equally essential for two purposes during the spacecraft flight: it must accept the tracking information from the world-wide tracking network, reducing the direction and distance information provided by the network into an hour-by-hour location of the spacecraft in space. This continuing calculation of the spacecraft's location can then be plotted to show what its actual trajectory is. The actual trajectory, of course, is compared with the predicted or planned trajectory to determine how far off course the original launch has put the spacecraft and, equally, to establish the correction necessary to bring it back to an acceptable course. Once this correction is established, the computer goes to work again to develop mathematically the commands that must be given to the spacecraft to change its trajectory to bring it more nearly in line with the planned trajectory. These commands are based on the same factors of gravitational influence, mass of the spacecraft, thrust and time of firing of the auxiliary rocket, etc., used to determine what the correction maneuver should be. All must be calculated very precisely and for some future instant in time so that when the command is given to the spacecraft it will be executed properly in the circumstances in which the spacecraft finds itself at that time.

In addition, the computers also are busily occupied in processing data which are telemetered from the spacecraft, reporting both the findings of its scientific instruments and the state of its own health and operations. Such things as level of battery charge, amount of electric power coming in from the solar panels, the heat (or chill) of various operating components, the angle of various antennas, and the aim of various instruments are all transmitted to earth as digital data which are converted by the computer to code words that convey the information.

A typical computing facility required to do all these things must process over 90 million binary bits of computer data, approximating 13 million data words, during a mission to a nearby planet.

There are three major subsystems required in this kind of a computer installation. The first is the primary computing facility which handles all the tracking data, the calculation of the actual trajectory, the comparison of the actual trajectory with the planned trajectory, and the computation of correction maneuvers and the commands necessary to accomplish these maneuvers. A second subsytem essentially duplicates the first and is kept on stand-by in case the first fails at a critical period in the space flight mission. Usually this stand-by subsystem is used in parallel with the primary system during these critical phases such as launch, orbit determination, and conduct of

```
QDGZXXDRDXDRA Z DSQSGIGGGQXRGLZOX DXQ XZAIZGAVAQQSXZXXDRDZDRA S
ZSQSGIGGGQXRDRQOX DXQ XQAIZGAVQQKVA XXDRDZDRANGDSSQSGIGGGQXRDIZO
A DNQ XZAIZAZZZQKDZ XXDRDDDRZLQ ZSQSGIGGGGXRGVZOA DNQ XZARZGAVQQ
KVKZXXDLKKDRK A ZSQSGIGGGGXRGVQOA DNQ XZARZGAVQKZZAZXXDRZDDRA S
ZSQSGIGGGGXRGZQOA DNQ XZARZAZVAKDDGZXXDRDADIZLA DSQSGIGGGGXRGZQO
A DNQ XZARZAZVAKDSSZXXDRDDDRXOS DSQSQIGGGGXRDDZOA DNQ XZARZXAVQK
ZVA XXDRDZDRANGDSSQSGSGGGGXRDSQOG DXQ XZARZXAVAKDZDZXXDRDLDRA Z
DSQSAQGGGGXRDSQOG DXQ XZARZXAZZKZZDZXXDLKADRA Z DSQSGIGGGGXRGXOO
C DXQ XZAIZXAVSKDZGZXXDRZXDRZ Z DSQSAQGGGGXRDAZOG DXQ XZAIZAZVAK
  ASHOZDA LDDGZXXDRDXDRA Z DSQSGIGGGXRDGSOG DXQ XZA ZAZVQKZSSZ
XXDRDDDRZ   ADGI SGIGGGXRDGAOG DXQ XZAIZAZVQKZVA XXDRDZDRANGDSSQS
GIGGGGXRDQAOQ DXQ XZAIZXAZZKZZD XXDRDLZDZHA DSQSGIGGGGXRDQAOQ DX
Q XZAVZXZVQKZZD XXDLKADRKHQ ZSQSGIGGGGXRDKZOQ DXQ XZAVZAAVQKZZGZ
XXDRZXDRZ S ZSQSGIGGGXRS ZOQ DXQ XZAIZAZVQKZDG XXDRDSDIZ A ZSQS
GIGXGGXRS ZOQ DXQ XZAIZAZVQQKSX XXDRDDDRZNS ZSQSGIGGGGXRSOAOQ DX
Q XZAVZAAZZQKVA XXDRDZDRANGDSSQSAQGGGGXRSOAOK DNQ XZAVZAAVQQKZZZ
XXDRDLDRA Z DSQSAQGGGGXRSNZOK DNQ XZAIZAZSQQZSZXXDLKADRA Z DSQS
AQGGGGXRSNZOK DNQ XZAIZGAVQQKZG XXDRZXDRZ Z DSQSAQGGGGXRSLAOK DN
Q XZAIZAZZZQKDG XXDRDSDRZ Z DSQSAQGGGGXRSLAOK DNQ XZAIZAZZZQKSSZ
XXDRDZDRA S ZSQSGIGGGXRSLAOK DNQ XZAIZAZZZQKVA XXDRDZDRANGDSSQS
  AGHOZDAHSAGSGGGGXRSIZHZ DXQ XZAIZAZZZQKQQZXXDRDNDRZNQ DSQSGSGX
GGXRSIQHZ DXQ XZAIZXAZSQQZXZXXDLKQDRSQS ZSQSGIGGGQXRSVAHZ DXQ XZ
AVZAADSQKZGZXXDRZSDRA S ZSQSXSGGGQXRSVAHZ DXQ XZAGZAG ZQKDG XXDR
DSDIZLZ ZSQSSQGGGQXRSDQHZ DXQ XQGHZGGHZQQSX XXDRDIDRXIS ZSQSDHGG
  GQXRQDAHZ DXQ XQGLZQGHAQKVA XXDRDZDRANGDSSQSZSGGGQXRQSAHD DNQ XQ
GLZQGHAKZZKZXXDRDDDRZ Z DSQSZIGGGQXRQSAHD DNQ XQGHZQGHZKDZXZXXDL
KGDRZ Z DSQSZSGGGQXRSAZHD DNQ XQAZZQZQSKDZGZXXDRZDDRA Z DSQSSHGG
GQXRSAQHD DNQ XQARZQAZQKZDG XXDRDSDRZ Z DSQSXIGGQOXRSGAHD DNQ XZ
ARZGAZZKZSX XXDRDIDRZ S ZSQSAHGGQOXRQGQHD DNQ XZALZAAZZKZVA XXDR
```

A sample of data telemetered from a spacecraft in flight. (*Jet Propulsion Laboratory*)

any trajectory-correction maneuver. Thus, in case of failure in one system—and computers do occasionally go haywire—the necessary information and answers would be simultaneously available from the parallel facility.

The third subsystem is the telemetry processing subsystem. This system accepts all the information telemetered from the spacecraft about both its scientific instrument readings and its own condition of health, reduces them to language understandable by humans, and prints them out in a manner similar to that of a teletype printer. It is these printouts that are under the surveillance of the six closed-circuit television cameras whose consoles are in the mission manager's control room.

In addition to the actual electronic computers, much peripheral equipment is required. This includes, for the technically minded, FM discriminators, code translators, analog-to-digital converters, magnetic-tape recorders, and punched-tape punches and readers with equipment to convert punched-tape information to magnetic tape and back again.

In a typical launch operation, the powered flight portion of the spacecraft's trajectory is first calculated as of the planned launch time minus five minutes (L–5). This calculation may have to be repeated several times because of "holds" due to real or suspected malfunctions in either the spacecraft, whose many complex instruments are being constantly monitored, or the launching-rocket booster.

When the spacecraft is actually launched, a preprogrammed orbit determination is calculated using the early inputs from the Cape Kennedy fast-tracking mobile units and the first down-range mobile unit. The calculations resulting from this computer run are used to direct the first permanent station of the DSIF in finding the spacecraft in flight.

Usually, during the first twelve hours following the launch, both the primary and secondary computer substations perform parallel computations on tracking data. This parallel computation is conducted for two reasons: as a safety backup of one computation by the second, and as a check on the performance of one computer complex by the other.

The secondary subsystem normally ceases operations twelve hours after launch, and does not begin operations again until a trajectory-correction maneuver has been determined to be necessary and the maneuver itself has been computed. Then, at the beginning of the correction-maneuver phase of the spacecraft's flight, the secondary subsystem is again put into operation parallel with the primary computing subsystem.

Normally, tracking data are processed daily (after the first twelve hours) and, on the results of this processing, trajectory-correction maneuver studies are conducted daily until the trajectory-correction maneuver is actually completed.

Once this critical period is past, if the spacecraft mission is a long one, such as to a near planet (but not the moon), tracking data are then processed only once a week to confirm that the spacecraft continues in the trajectory planned for it.

A few days before the spacecraft is expected to encounter the planet toward which it has been sent, the computing tempo is stepped up again. Usually tracking data are again processed daily until a few hours before the time of the planned encounter with the target planet. At this point tracking data are processed continually in near-real time throughout the encounter period, tapering off on a daily basis for several days thereafter.

If the encounter is productive of a great deal of scientific or engineering data, the secondary computing subsystem may be used to handle tracking data while the primary system assists the telemetry subsystem in processing telemetered data. This arrangement is made simply because the volume of information telemetered may exceed the capacity of one computer subsystem.

The activities of the telemetry subsystem are slightly different from those of the tracking subsystem in a typical mission. Under present launching conditions, the DSIF station near Johannesburg, South Africa, first receives the telemetry signal, demodulates it, and puts it in the proper form for teletype transmission to the computation center at the JPL. The other DSIF stations follow in sequence as the spacecraft is sighted from their installations.

The telemetry data, reporting both on scientific experiments aboard the spacecraft and on the condition of the spacecraft itself are received and processed twenty-four hours a day, seven days a week—in contrast to the periodic reporting of tracking data.

A high-speed microfilm unit is used to prepare "quick-look" copy of the computer printout within thirty minutes of receipt of the raw data by the DSIF network. These "quick-look" printouts are reviewed by the spacecraft data analysis team and by the scientific-data team. The first team, of course, is concerned with the operating condition of the spacecraft, while the second team is concerned with what the scientific instruments aboard the spacecraft are reporting about conditions in space through which the spacecraft is passing.

These reports from the spacecraft are presented to the interested teams at intervals of 30 minutes; the computer processing and delivery time requires from 4½ to 7 minutes, depending upon the complexity of the data and the complexity of the program required for reduction of data to a form understandable by the teams.

It is obvious from the foregoing discussion that much of the information that we get from a spacecraft, either about its own performance or about the space environment through which it passes, is sent to earth by a technique called telemetry. Telemetry is a coined word meaning "telegraphed measurements." Early developments in telemetry can probably be ascribed to the need to know how missiles behaved in flight.

In the days when winged aircraft were the chief flight vehicles in which we were interested, we built one as well as we knew how, put a pilot in it and told him to fly it. If the pilot survived, he could come back and tell the designers and engineers how the plane behaved in flight.

With the advent of missiles, however, it was impossible to put a man aboard to do this reporting. Efforts were first made to monitor a missile's performance with cameras, both on the ground and in the missile itself. While these photographic records were of some help, they could not provide all the information that was needed on missile performance.

Consequently, missile developers began to install in the missile minute "pickups" or transducers, as they are called technically, to measure such things as temperature, spin rate, missile attitude (pitch, roll, and yaw), as well as the air pressure and turbulence at various points along the missile body and control surfaces. These pickups were called transducers because they converted pressure, temperature, or position readings into electrical impulses. With this accomplished, the next step was to put a miniaturized, frequency-modulated radio transmitter into the missile which would accept all these electrical inputs from the various transducers and rebroadcast them to a receiving station on the ground. At this point, just as in spacecraft telemetry, the signals would be demodulated and interpreted.

Usually the output of the various transducers is sampled on a programmed basis—a sample from transducer 1 is accepted and rebroadcast, then a sample from transducer 2 is accepted and rebroadcast, etc., until the entire pattern has been completed.

Because these transducer signals are applied to a high-frequency radio carrier wave by frequency modulation, they can produce, at the receiving station, a somewhat musical output, varying in tone as transducer response after transducer response is demodulated.

When this technique is applied to the many instruments and operation monitors aboard a spacecraft, the resulting output resembles a random series of musical chords, which one prominent space scientist has described as "the music of the spheres."

5. Propulsion and Power

Someone once defined rocket propulsion as a controlled explosion. Occasionally the control goes awry, as attested by the shattering explosion of an Atlas on the pad at Cape Kennedy. Reinforced-concrete blockhouses are necessary to protect the launch-control personnel at any rocket launching site.

The awe-inspiring and (until you have experienced it) unbelievable man-made thunder of a big rocket blasting off in a veritable bath of flame is unmatched as a display of raw power by any other peaceful human activity. As the plans of the rocket developers mature, these spectacular displays will become more awe-inspiring, more gaudy, and increasingly more thunderous—at least where chemical rockets are concerned.

For the foreseeable future, every spacecraft will have to be boosted into orbit, or injected into its deep-space trajectory, by a rocket making use of chemical reactions as the source of its power. Once in orbit or embarked upon its trajectory, the spacecraft may then be propelled faster and faster toward its objective by nuclear or electric (plasma) propulsion devices, which are most effective for the long journey to far planets or possibly to the nearer stars.

Propulsion devices may generally be divided into three classes: the chemical rockets, with their short bursts of tremendous power intended primarily to lift the spacecraft out of the immediate influence of earth's gravity; the nuclear and electric propulsion devices which have very low thrust compared to the chemical rockets, but which

103

can continue operating over long periods of time, thus accelerating a spacecraft in powered flight to speeds which are a significant fraction of the speed of light (186,000 miles per second). Even more exotic propulsion devices, which at present are only dreams of their would-be designers, may employ such principles as that of "solar sails" responsive to the solar wind or that of antigravity.

Propulsion systems in the first two classes described above are commonly known as reaction motors, or reaction engines. They are based on the physical law that for every action there is an equal and opposite reaction. Thus, in the chemical rocket, for example, as the flaming gases which are the product of oxidation in the rocket's combustion chamber are blasted out of the rocket nozzles at speeds of several thousand feet per second, the reaction of the rocket body is to move in the opposite direction. Mathematically, the velocity of the rocket gases multiplied by their mass (weight) gives a product which, when divided by the mass of the rocket itself, gives a dividend which is the rocket speed in a direction opposite to that of the escaping gases. The rocket speed, of course, is reduced by the pull of the earth's gravity if the rocket is proceeding in a direction away from the pull of gravity.

Chemical rockets are generally divided into two classes: liquid-propellant and solid-propellant. The most usual construction of liquid-propellant rockets employs two tanks, one for the rocket fuel and the other for the fuel oxidizer, the latter necessary because the rocket normally progresses out of the atmosphere very rapidly into space where there is not sufficient oxygen to burn the fuel. The fuel itself is generally a hydrocarbon somewhat like kerosene; the oxidizer is usually oxygen extracted from the air and cooled and compressed until it is liquid, so that a great amount of it may be stored in a relatively small space. Work is also being done with so-called monopropellants, which contain in one fluid both the fuel and the oxidizer.

Solid-propellant rockets generally contain a fuel and an oxidizer gelled in a rubber-like plastic compound to give them form and stability. The plastic compound also helps to control the burning rate. (Control of burning rate is the difference between a controlled explosion and an explosion.)

Liquid-propellant rockets originally offered the advantage of the capability of being shut off and restarted while in flight; thus, all their power did not have to be used in one single burst, and the restart capability made possible certain maneuvers which were important to getting a rocket into the proper trajectory.

Solid-propellant rocket engines had an original advantage of "storability" (liquid oxygen cannot be kept liquid in storage unless it is possible to maintain it at temperatures near absolute zero and under great pressure). For several years it was believed impossible to stop and restart a solid-propellant rocket engine, but this capability has recently been made available in solid-propellant rocket engines of modern design.

By comparison with the chemical-fueled rockets, the nuclear and electric propulsion devices seem to have very low power. Although a physicist would wince at equating rocket thrust and horsepower, a rough approximation of eight horsepower per pound of thrust provides a convenient rule-of-thumb comparison. Thus, the 360,000-pound thrust developed by the Atlas D missile, commonly used as a spacecraft booster, is roughly equivalent to 3 million horsepower. Future chemical boosters, designed specifically for space exploration, may have thrusts as high as 12 million pounds, roughly equivalent to 100 million horsepower.

By comparison with these fantastic figures, the thrust of nuclear and electric propulsion devices seems minuscule. In the relatively frictionless environment of space, where gravitational pulls more or less balance each other out, a thrust capable of giving an acceleration only one-tenth that attributable to gravity at the earth's surface can, in time, propel a spacecraft to speeds almost unimaginable. The acceleration of gravity at the earth's surface is 32 feet per second per second; this is 1 g, and means that a falling body will be traveling at the rate of 32 feet per second at the end of the first second of fall, 64 feet per second at the end of the second second, and 96 feet per second at the end of the third second, etc. Thus, if friction with the atmosphere (wind resistance) did not limit this acceleration, a body accelerated at the rate of 1 g would be traveling at the rate of 640 feet per second at the end of the twentieth second—a speed of a little over 400 miles per hour. In actual fact, however, bodies moving through the earth's atmosphere under the influence of gravitational acceleration reach a "terminal velocity." This is the velocity at which the drag of the air balances the acceleration of gravity; for a sky diver parachuting out of an airplane this terminal velocity is approximately 200 miles an hour, which is reached by approximately the end of the tenth second of fall. Other objects, depending upon their streamlined design and density, have other terminal velocities in the earth's atmosphere.

Outside the earth's atmosphere, however, in the extremely tenuous and almost frictionless fluid of space, resistance of the medium is not so great a factor, and a relatively small acceleration can produce tremendous speed. An acceleration of $1/10$ g, or 3.2 feet per second per second would, at the end of 100 seconds, produce a velocity increment of 320 feet per second. But 100 seconds is only a little over a minute and a half. Imagine, if you will, a $1/10$ g acceleration applied over a period of a month. The attained velocity at the end of a month would be 8,294,400 feet per second or 1,570 miles per second. At these velocities, and even higher speeds which will be reached on trips to the far planets or nearby stars, streamlining of the spaceship may become important because travel through the tenuous fluid of space at these high speeds produces the same shock waves and other phenomena which we associate with rapid travel through the fluid of air or water.

Before we get too far off among the distant planets and nearer stars, let us consider some of the big chemical reaction engines which are under construction or are being planned for use in the space program.

NASA Chemical Rockets

The National Aeronautics and Space Administration (NASA) has settled on a series of twelve basic launch vehicles. They are called the Scout, Delta, Thor-Agena B, Thor-Ablestar, Atlas D, Atlas-Agena B, Titan II, Titan III, Centaur, Saturn, Advanced Saturn, and Nova.

The Scout is the smallest vehicle in this basic series. It was designed to provide a relatively inexpensive launch vehicle for near-earth probes and satellites. The Scout has four stages: the first stage, Algol II-A, has a thrust of 86,000 pounds at sea level; the thrust of the second stage, Castor, is 64,000 pounds; the third stage, Antares, 23,000 pounds; and the fourth stage, Altair, 3,000 pounds. Excluding the fins, the Scout has a maximum diameter of 3.3 feet; its height is 65 feet (without payload); and it can put a payload of 200 pounds into a 300 nautical-mile earth orbit.

Some of the missions for which the Scout has been used include scientific satellites of the Explorer series and micrometeorite and ionosphere studies. The Scout has also been used to loft probes to study re-entry heating, electric engines, and life sciences. The improvements in the engines of the Scout and the use of new high-energy solid propellants have raised the original Scout capability from 200 to 300 pounds in a 300-mile orbit.

The Delta is a three-stage rocket, using liquid oxygen and kerosene for the first stage to produce a thrust of 170,000 pounds; the second stage employs a propellant called unsymmetrical dimethylhydrazine and inhibited red fuming nitric acid to produce a thrust of 7,700 pounds; the third stage is the solid-propellant Altair (which is the fourth stage of the Scout), producing a thrust of approximately 3,000 pounds.

This vehicle is 88 feet tall and 8 feet in diameter; it can lift an 800-pound payload into a 350 nautical-mile orbit or boost a 130-pound payload to escape velocity.

The Delta vehicle has been used to launch satellites of the Echo, Tiros, Explorer, and Telstar series. It was also used to put the OSO, the Orbiting Solar Observatory, into a 340/370-mile orbit. The Telstar, of course, is a private communications satellite of the American Telephone and Telegraph Company, but it was launched for that company by NASA.

Next in size is the two-stage Thor-Agena B. In this vehicle, the liquid oxygen and kerosene first stage produces a thrust of 170,000 pounds; the second stage (like that of the Delta) uses unsymmetrical

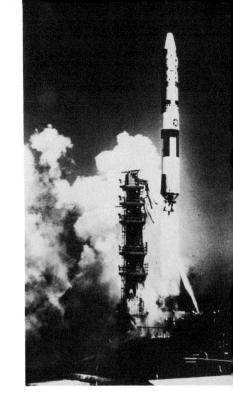

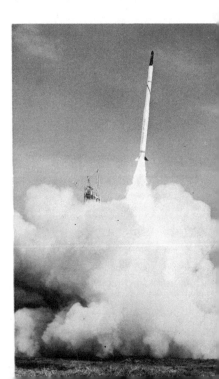

Eight of the NASA family of rocket boosters. (*NASA photos*)

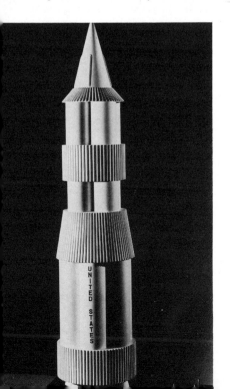

dimethylhydrazine and inhibited red fuming nitric acid to produce a thrust of 16,000 pounds. The vehicle is 76 feet tall and has a diameter of 8 feet, excluding fins.

The Thor-Agena B is used primarily for launching meteorological, communications, and scientific satellites. Some of the missions it has launched include the topside ionospheric sounder, the Polar-Orbiting Geophysical Observatory (POGO), the nimbus cloud study, and the rigidized-sphere Echo satellite.

The launch vehicle which is most familiar to millions of television viewers, of course, is the Atlas D, which has been used to launch the manned Mercury capsules. The Atlas is a modification of the Air Force's intercontinental ballistic missile.

The Atlas D is called a 1½-stage vehicle. It has one main engine. Two auxiliary engines are attached on opposite sides of the main engine to form the half stage. All three of these engines are ignited at launch, but the outer two are jettisoned at the end of their burning period; while the sustainer (main) engine continues to burn until orbital velocity is achieved. The main engine is a liquid oxygen and kerosene booster with a thrust of 367,000 pounds at sea level. The maximum diameter of the main engine is 10 feet. With the two auxiliary engines attached, the rocket is 16 feet across at the base; the height is 72 feet. It is capable of putting a 2,700-pound payload into a 100 nautical-mile orbit.

As used to launch the Mercury capsule in which John Glenn and other astronauts blazed their way into orbit, a tower is added to the top of the Atlas above the capsule. In this tower is a system to sense any malfunction in the performance of the Atlas and to lift the Mercury capsule free of the vehicle. The addition of the Mercury capsule and its escape tower increases the length of the Atlas from its original 72 feet to a total of 95¼ feet. The Atlas D will probably not be used as a space booster since the Mercury series of spacecraft launchings was completed early in 1963.

The Atlas-Agena B, however, will continue to be one of the workhorses of the NASA program for some time to come. Atlas-Agena B functions will be the launching of lunar missions and communications and scientific satellites.

The Atlas-Agena B is a two-stage rocket using the same liquid propellants as the Thor-Agena B. The first stage develops a thrust of 367,000 pounds with a sustaining thrust of 80,000 pounds, while the Agena B second stage develops a thrust of 16,000 pounds. The diameter of the vehicle is 10 feet (16 feet maximum including the auxiliary engines) and its height is 91 feet. It is capable of lifting a 6,000 pound payload into a 300 nautical-mile orbit; it can boost 750 pounds to escape velocity or launch a payload of 425 pounds to the vicinity of the planets Mars or Venus.

Missions in which it has been and will be used include the Eccentric Geophysical Observatory (EGO), the Orbiting Astronomical Observatory, an advanced passive-communications satellite, lunar missions of the Ranger spacecraft, and planetary missions of the Mariner spacecraft, both to Venus and to Mars.

The single-chamber Agena engine, comprising the second stage, may be shut off and re-started in space.

In a typical lunar mission all three engines of the Atlas are ignited at liftoff. The two outer engines burn for about two and a half minutes and then drop away. The sustainer engine burns for another two minutes, by which time the vehicle has reached an altitude of approximately 80 miles. Ever since liftoff two small engines of about 1,000 pounds thrust each have been helping; and, after main engine cutoff, for about thirty seconds they continue to make fine adjustments in the velocity of the vehicle. These small vernier engines are shut off by guidance command. Simultaneously an onboard computer starts the timer on the Agena stage in the Atlas' airborne guidance system.

After vernier cutoff, the aerodynamic nose cone protecting the payload is discarded. Agena is separated from the Atlas first stage by explosive charges. Retrorockets cause the Atlas shell to drop back so that it does not interfere with the subsequent maneuvers of the Agena. The guidance system, working through small maneuvering jets, brings the Agena into horizontal alignment with the surface of the earth.

As soon as this maneuver is accomplished, the onboard computer ignites the Agena engine for a first burning period of two and a half minutes; during this period, of course, the guidance system keeps the Agena pointed in the right direction by using an infrared horizon-sensing device. At the end of the two and a half minutes, the payload is in an earth-circling "parking" orbit, approximately 100 miles up.

After a predetermined coasting period in the parking orbit, the Agena engine is re-ignited by the onboard computer or by command from the earth and powers the payload for another one and a half minutes, placing it in a proper trajectory for approach to the moon. Approximately two and a half minutes later the payload is separated from the Agena and continues by itself toward the vicinity of the moon. A similar sequence of events is used in launching a spacecraft toward the planets Venus or Mars.

Like the Atlas, the Titan II is a military (Air Force) intercontinental ballistic missile which has been modified by NASA for launching of the two-man Gemini spacecraft. This two-stage rocket uses storable liquid propellants (a mixture of unsymmetrical dimethylhydrazine and hydrazine as a fuel, and nitrogen tetroxide as the oxidizer). The first stage develops 430,000 pounds of thrust at sea level and the second stage develops 100,000 pounds of thrust. The Titan II's maximum diameter is 10 feet, and the height is 115 feet; it is capable of lifting more than 6,000 pounds into a low earth orbit. The first stage is powered by two 215,000-pound-thrust rocket engines; the second stage is powered by a single 100,000-pound-thrust engine.

Because the Titan II's propellants are storable and ignite on contact, it can be launched on short notice, thus reducing the length of the countdown. The Titan II makes it possible for United States astronauts to practice rendezvousing two spacecraft in orbit, a type of exercise necessary as a prelude to the Apollo program, in which we expect to send men into a lunar orbit where one spacecraft will rendezvous with another.

All of the rocket vehicles previously described have been military weapons which have had minimum modification and then, in some cases, have been combined with upper stages which were developed separately.

Following the Titan II is the Titan III. It is the first rocket vehicle to be developed by the Department of Defense specifically for use as a space booster. The Titan III was originally planned to launch into earth orbit the Dynasoar spacecraft, X-20, of the Air Force. The Titan III is really a cluster of five rockets plus a control module. The basic vehicle is the two-stage Titan II plus a third stage producing 16,000 pounds of thrust. In addition to these three elements, a pair of 120-inch diameter solid-propellant motors are "strapped on" to opposite sides of the Titan II vehicle to provide additional boost on liftoff. Each of the solid motors develops over 1 million pounds of thrust, and the Titan II, of course, develops 430,000 pounds of thrust; consequently the combination will have a total thrust of approximately 2.5 million pounds at sea level.

The height of the Titan III, without the Dynasoar or other spacecraft, is somewhat more than 100 feet. The diameter—or rather the maximum width—is 30 feet, and it is capable of lifting 25,000 pounds into a low earth orbit.

The first launching of a manned space vehicle with the Titan III is planned for 1965 by the Air Force. In addition to the Titan, as described above, the program calls for development of the powerful new solid-propellant "core" booster to replace the presently used storable liquid-propellant core.

The Centaur rocket vehicle, as originally conceived, was to consist of an Atlas first-stage redesigned to carry a new kind of upper stage producing almost twice the thrust of the Agena B. This upper stage was to use liquid hydrogen as propellant or fuel and liquid oxygen as oxidizer. Despite the great theoretical promise of this combination the actual use of it has demanded major research and development achievements which to date have been lagging behind schedule.

The Centaur, for example, was originally expected to carry the Mariner spacecraft into trajectory for its fly-by of the planet Venus; because of its tardy development, however, the Mariner mission to Venus was powered by the Atlas-Agena B. As designed, the Centaur is 100 feet high, 10 feet in diameter, and has the Atlas D's 367,-000-pound thrust at sea level liftoff, with the Centaur upper stage providing 30,000 pounds of thrust.

Even the Centaur, while it was planned primarily for space operations rather than military operations, was nevertheless assembled around that original military workhorse, the Atlas intercontinental ballistic missile.

The Saturn, on the other hand, might be called a new generation of rocket boosters; it was designed specifically for space booster use and, while it made use of knowledge gained with previous military and military-adapted rockets, it is essentially a new design and a new type of construction.

The Saturn has been developed in two configurations, called the C-1 and the C-1B. Both these rockets make use of the "cluster" principle of grouping a number of smaller rocket engines in a single launching vehicle.

The Saturn C-1 is a two-stage rocket in which the first stage consists of eight clustered H-1 engines, using liquid oxygen as oxidizer and kerosene as fuel. The second stage, utilizing liquid oxygen and liquid hydrogen (like the second stage of the Centaur) develops 90,000 pounds of thrust. The first stage develops 1.5 million pounds at sea level.

The maximum diameter of the Saturn, excluding fins, is 21.6 feet, the height is 125 feet, and it is capable of lifting 20,000 pounds, or 10 tons, into a 300 nautical-mile orbit.

When fully operational, the Saturn is expected to be used to put in earth orbit spacecraft which will then take off on their own to land men upon the moon. It may also be used to transport the components of earth-orbiting space stations into orbits where they may be joined to form complete space stations. This vehicle first successfully orbited a payload of 37,500 pounds on January 29, 1964.

The Saturn C-1B configuration is essentially a larger version of the two-stage C-1. The chief difference is in the second stage, where the thrust has been boosted from 90,000 pounds to 200,000 pounds; the first-stage cluster of H-1 engines will still produce 1.5 million pounds of thrust at sea level. The diameter is the same as the C-1, but the height has been increased to 150 feet. With this stronger second stage, the Saturn C-1B can boost into a 100 nautical-mile orbit 32,000 pounds of payload.

Its use is somewhat the same as the Saturn C-1: to launch into earth orbit the Apollo spacecraft and its lunar excursion module. Saturn C-1B, of course, will also be used as a sort of space freight car to haul into the proper orbit the necessary equipment, materials, and supplies needed for missions which land men on the moon.

Another member of the Saturn family is called the Advanced Saturn. This three-stage launch vehicle is the first of the really big space vehicles, having a maximum diameter of 33 feet, excluding fins, and a height of 280 feet. The first-stage thrust is 7.5 million pounds, the second stage is 1 million pounds, and the third stage is 200,000 pounds. The first stage is fueled with kerosene with a liquid-oxygen oxidizer, while the second and third stages are liquid-oxygen/liquid-hydrogen engines.

The first stage comprises five F-1 engines, each producing 1.5 million pounds of thrust. The second stage is a cluster of five J-2 engines, each producing 200,000 pounds of thrust. The third stage is a single J-2 engine.

This huge machine will be capable of putting 120 tons into a 100/300-mile earth orbit; it can send a spacecraft weighing 45 tons on missions to the moon, or it can boost a 35-ton spacecraft into a trajectory aimed at the nearby planets.

As of this writing the F-1 engines making up the Advanced Saturn's first stage have been static-fired in tests which proved highly successful. This amazing engine can produce singly the amount of thrust produced by the eight H-1 engines in the Saturn C-1 or C-1B.

It is believed that the noise energy from an Advanced Saturn launching will be so tremendous that it will kill a man at fifty miles if he is unprotected by a suitable insulated structure. This problem has led a number of aerospace organizations to suggest that the Advanced Saturn be launched at sea from a barge or from some specially designed stable platform so that at takeoff the vehicle can be far from inhabited areas.

The manned spacecraft atop this tremendous machine would have to be carefully constructed to protect the passengers against this sound energy at the moment of blastoff but, of course, within a few seconds they would be traveling faster than the speed of sound and therefore would be safe from vibrations occurring behind them at the loud nozzles of this gargantuan rocket.

Present plans are for the Advanced Saturn to put the Apollo spacecraft into orbit around the moon; from the lunar-orbiting Apollo, the two-man lunar excursion module will descend to the surface of the moon, conduct tests, make surface explorations, and, on its own rocket power, return its passengers to the Apollo for the journey back to earth.

If the capabilities of the Advanced Saturn strain credulity, the concept of the even bigger Nova launch vehicle is almost beyond

The mighty Rocketdyne F-1 engine with 1.5 million pounds of thrust in a static night test at Edwards Test Station, California. (*Rocketdyne Division of North American Aviation, Inc.*)

imagining. The Nova is planned to have a weight-lifting capability two to three times that of the Advanced Saturn, making it capable of putting about 300 tons of payload into an earth orbit, sending a 100-ton spacecraft to the moon, or putting a 75- to 100-ton spacecraft on a trajectory to Mars or Venus.

The dimensions of the Nova are expected to be a diameter of approximately 50 feet and a height of approximately 300 feet. Both liquid and solid propellants are being considered for use in the first stage; the ultimate decision will probably depend upon competitive advances in these two types of propulsion engines between now and the time when the design must be "frozen." The second and third stages will probably employ the high-energy liquid-oxygen/liquid-hydrogen propellants in engines first utilized for the Centaur.

Because of the noise problems mentioned in connection with the Advanced Saturn, the Nova would almost certainly have to be launched at sea or in some very remote location.

Because of its capability of putting big payloads into an interplanetary trajectory, Nova will be designed so that it can accept a nuclear-powered third stage, or a third stage using some other of the exotic and advanced propulsion techniques.

With the mighty thunder of the chemical rockets fading into the distance of interplanetary space, let us turn our attention toward the quieter, but equally potent exotic propulsion systems which may one day enable man to reach the nearer stars.

Nuclear and Electric Rockets

Since the problem of lifting heavy spacecraft into an orbit which balances the earth's pull of gravity or into a trajectory which allows the spacecraft to escape from that pull is so far a requirement which demands the sudden and powerful thrust of chemical rocket engines, the so-called exotic engines are being considered primarily as sources of in-flight propulsion or auxiliary power.

While much work is being done in research and development of exotic propulsion engines—a few of them have even been flown in an experimental form—there is not at this writing a nuclear or electric engine of size, power, and efficiency to make it practical for use in an actual mission.

When we speak of nuclear or electric, the line between the two is not very clearly drawn because they sometimes supplement each other.

In both the nuclear and electric engines, the simplest type operates by heating a gas so that it expands and is expelled through a supersonic nozzle to produce thrust. If you stop to think about it, this is exactly what a chemical engine does: the process of combustion between the fuel and the oxidizer heats the resulting gases so that they expand tremendously and are expelled at high velocity through the rocket nozzle, producing thrust which drives the booster or spacecraft in a direction opposite to that in which the escaping gas is traveling. The only difference, then, between chemical engines and these most primitive kinds of nuclear and electric engines is that the source of the heat is different: instead of relying on chemical combusion for the heat, it is derived from a nuclear reaction or from an electrical current.

Nuclear engines are generally of two types. In the very simplest types the heat of the nuclear reaction is brought into direct contact, through a thin-walled chamber, with the propellant gas, such as argon, in a heating chamber which is connected to a nozzle. It is the rapid passage of the heated gas through this nozzle which provides the thrust to drive the spacecraft.

A slightly more sophisticated nuclear engine operates somewhat like the conventional steam turbine, heating a fluid which turns a turbine attached to an electrical generator, producing an electrical current which by one means or another heats the gas used to drive the spacecraft.

In a simple form of electrothermal engine called a resisto jet, the electrical current is run through a coil of wire similar to that in a portable electric heater. In the resisto jet, however, the coil of resistance wire forms the inside wall of the heating chamber through which the gas is passed. Coming in contact with the heated coil of wire, the gas expands and rushes out of the nozzle to provide thrust. A slightly more involved electrothermal engine uses the electric current to create an arc as in the electric arc "searchlight" whose gleaming bars of light against the night sky attracts attention to the opening of a Hollywood hamburger stand.

The electric-arc mechanism is designed somewhat differently in an arc jet engine, however. In the arc jet, one of the electrodes, the cathode, lies along the axis of the gas-heating chamber, pointing toward the restriction in the nozzle. The other electrode, the anode, is the restrictive part of the nozzle itself. Gas is injected through the sides of the gas-heating chamber, flows through the electrical arc between the cathode and the anode, and is heated in the process. This heating causes the gas to expand so that it rushes out the nozzle at supersonic speeds, providing the thrust which drives the arc-jet engine.

Both the resisto jet and the arc jet, just described, can draw their electrical power from sources other than a nuclear reactor. Some of these sources are solar cells and fuel cells.

However, in the present state of development, those engines using heat to activate some turbo machinery to produce electrical power are currently favored. The names of some of the projects using this principle are Snap, Spur, Sunflower and Aztec.

In the electrothermal engines described above, a gas is used as propellant. Since space is such a high vacuum there is not enough of any gas there to run effectively one of the engines just described. Consequently, these engines have to carry their own gas supply with them. Current experiments seem to indicate that the most practical gas for this purpose is argon. Argon requires less voltage, for example, to maintain a continuous arc through the flow of gas. Argon, too, provides a higher specific impulse (roughly equivalent to a horsepower-to-weight ratio) than some gases. In addition, argon is more easily stored than some other gases.

It is a rather amazing and interesting fact that arc jets have been studied for perhaps 150 years, with interest in them being much more intense, of course, under the present demands of the space age.

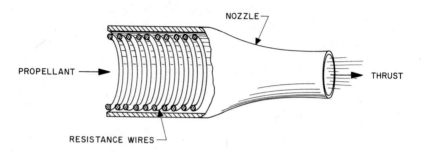

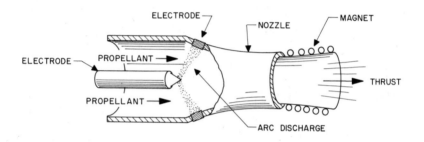

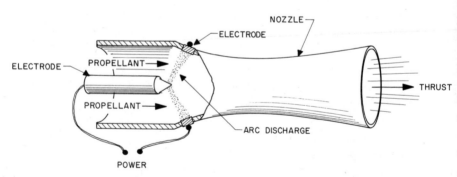

Diagram showing different types of nuclear-electric jets: (*Top*) the resisto jet; (*middle*) the arc jet; (*bottom*) the plasma jet. Thrust arrows show direction of particle flow; thrust exerted on the rocket is in the opposite direction.

Another kind of electric propulsion is called the plasma jet or ion engine. In this engine the gas is not only heated as in the resisto jet or arc jet, but is given added velocity by the application of a magnetic field in the area of the arc as a means of controlling the jet and giving it added energy.

Exotic Propulsion Systems

In its present form, the plasma jet or ion engine also has to carry its own supply of gas propellants. However, a recent concept developed by Electro-Optical Systems, Pasadena, California, envisions an exotic plasma engine which will take in the relatively thin and low-energy plasma which makes up the sea of energy in space, and by electromagnetic means increase its energy and the velocity of its particles, expelling them out of a nozzle to produce thrust. If this concept can be embodied in an actual design it will make it possible to move much greater payloads at much higher speeds than with other electric propulsion schemes, because this new engine will not have to carry its own propellant supply with it, but will find it in the stuff of which space is made. This concept may be likened, in part, to that of the jet engine on conventional air-breathing airplanes, which takes air in at the front of the engine, heats it to a high temperature by combining it with fuel in the combustion chamber, and expels it through the jet nozzle to push the plane forward. In the space-plasma engine, a low-energy plasma would be taken in the "front" of the engine as it travels through space, be given increased energy by the application of an electromagnetic field which drew its power perhaps from solar cells, and expelled as high-speed particles through a nozzle to create the thrust driving the spacecraft.

Still another kind of exotic engine being considered for in-flight propulsion in the solar system is the solar sail. With the early satellites it was discovered that the pressure of the radiation from the sun was great enough slowly and continuously to change the shape of the satellite orbit around the earth. With this discovery, investigations were undertaken to devise a means for taking advantage of the

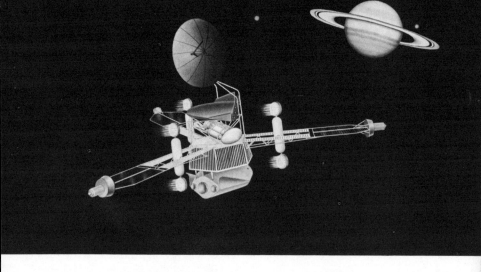

Proposed designs for
nuclear-powered space ship.
(*Jet Propulsion Laboratory*)

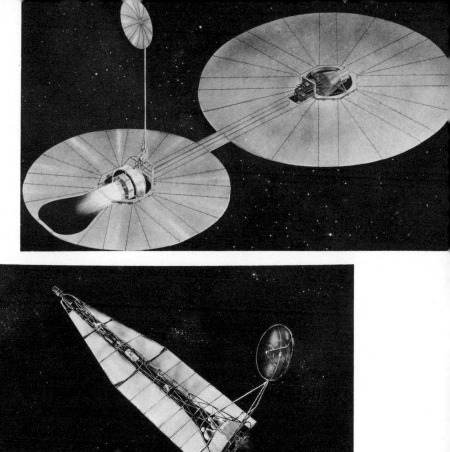

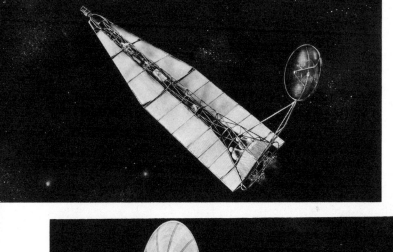

pressure of solar radiation to move a spacecraft through space in the vicinity of the sun. Of course, the farther the spacecraft gets from the sun the less effective solar radiation will be as a power source. This means that the solar sail will provide power only within the solar system, and probably only within the nearer reaches of the solar system; it is difficult to imagine, for example, that a solar sail could be a very effective means of propulsion at a distance as great as the orbit of Pluto, which is approximately four billion miles from the sun. Nevertheless, it is conceivable that a spacecraft might acquire sufficient momentum (inertia) from the action of the sun's radiation to carry it into some area of the heavens where the radiation from another star would become effective. It may even prove possible to devise an engine which responds to the pressure of cosmic radiation which reaches us from outside the solar system and is galactic or even intergalactic in origin.

For the present, resisto jets, arc jets, and solar sails are thought of chiefly in terms of making changes in the orbit of an earth satellite, shifting the plane of the orbit slightly, or enlarging or decreasing the length of the orbit. Arc jets may be useful for "freight car" missions to the moon some time in the future when really large space-borne electric power sources are developed; work is, of course, going ahead on this type of project. The plasma jets and ion engines, because they can operate over longer periods of time, are seen as having application for planetary or even interstellar missions.

Dr. Leonard D. Jaffe and Dwain F. Spencer of the JPL have proposed a multistage, nuclear-powered, plasma jet rocket (similar to the multistage chemical rockets) to achieve the great velocities necessary for interstellar travel.

Mathematically they have proved that a deuterium-fusion rocket of four or five stages could achieve a velocity approximately six-tenths that of the speed of light on an interstellar trip. This would mean a speed of about *111,600 miles per second!*

If this concept is actually turned into flyable hardware, such a spacecraft could theoretically reach our nearest star neighbor, Alpha Centauri, in only six or seven years travel time.

If such a spacecraft should carry humans (instead of mere instruments), it would, of course, have to be slowed down upon its arrival in the vicinity of Alpha Centauri. The slowing-down process would change a nominal 7-year trip into a 14½-year trip. The round trip to the star and back for such a nuclear-powered rocket transporting humans would thus require about twenty-nine years.

Actual travel to nearby stars may have to await the development of a practical nuclear-powered plasma jet which utilizes the thin plasma of space as its fuel (instead of carrying its own); or, an even more exotic development, an antigravity device which, with the flick of a switch, can reverse the effect of gravity, making it repel the spacecraft instead of attract it. With such a device a spacecraft could wander through the universe in a manner similar to Tarzan swinging from tree to tree in the jungle: He alternately pushes off from the limb he is leaving and pulls himself forward with the next vine he grasps. In a like manner, a spacecraft would be able, with an antigravity device, to push itself away from the earth or sun, until it was near enough to "grasp" the gravitational pull of the next heavenly body along its route. Repeating the process, it could travel through the universe indefinitely.

Traveling from galaxy to galaxy, however, really stretches the human imagination. As an example of the difficulties, the following comparison gives a good illustration:

At present, using *existing* propulsion systems and spacecraft, it requires approximately forty hours to travel from the earth to the moon. When we get to the point where we can make this trip in four hours—one-tenth of the present time required—we will be traveling at a speed which would take us to the *nearest* star in our own galaxy in 30,000 years.

Simply to cross our galaxy, the Milky Way, takes light 120,000 years; other galaxies have been detected by radio telescopes at distances as great as several *billion* light years from earth. Since scientists believe that the speed of light is the ultimate speed—nothing can go faster than light—it appears that we will have to confine our trips in space to other stars and their planets in our own galaxy.

6. Life in Space

When thinking about life in space there are at least two general classes of life to think about: one is the problem of maintaining earth man in space—his physical health, his mental and emotional well-being, and how to supply him with food, drink, and the comforts of home. The second major line of thought generally covers extraterrestrial life, or life not of this earth; this branch of study is called exobiology. Most people think of earth man or some other creature similar to earth man when they think of life in space; the study of exobiology is equally fascinating, however, and a great deal more work has been done on this than most people realize.

Earth Man in Space

Since we are chiefly concerned, however, with earth man in space or with our hopes of finding some creature similar to earth man in space, let us consider first the conditions that earth man has to maintain in order to exist either on earth or in space and how these conditions may be brought about.

There are relatively few basic factors that affect earth man's ability to exist and which permit him under ideal conditions to do more than simply exist—give him the surpluses of energy and time necessary to build great civilizations, create great art, and even consider visiting other planets and other stars.

First of all, his food must contain the chemical elements necessary

127

to maintain and build his bodily tissues and keep them functioning in the manner for which they were designed. Equally, he must have water to drink, for earth man's body is approximately 70 per cent water. This water is the basis for the many body fluids in which human cells live and the medium in which many of the life processes occur.

Even with protection in the form of clothes and housing, man has great difficulty in functioning normally when the temperature gets much lower than 30° F. below zero or much hotter than 120° F.

Earth man also needs a fairly calm and protective atmosphere. Life as we know it would be impossible on planets with winds commonly reaching four to eight hundred miles an hour or, conversely, on a planet with no air at all to shield man from some of the more deadly radiation from the sun and outer space and from meteorites which, if it were not for the atmosphere would strike the earth at speeds more than ten times that of the fastest rifle built and ten times more lethally. The chemical makeup of the atmosphere, too, must be compatible with earth man's life processes if he is to continue to exist; he could not, for example, survive in an atmosphere of ammonia or methane such as we know shrouds some of the planets in our solar system.

When you think of all the possible combinations of chemical elements which could make up a gaseous atmosphere or the kinds of liquids (other than water) from which planetary seas could be formed, or the extremes of temperature from 472° F. below zero (absolute zero) up to several million degrees as in the sun and other stars—it is apparent that earth man can exist only in a very narrow portion of the environmental spectrum. To venture out into space, earth man must take with him the kind of environment from which he has evolved and the only kind of environment in which he can now live.

The method for taking his own environment with him as man goes into space involves two kinds of containers in which man expects to be able to exist outside the earth's atmosphere and his accustomed environment.

The first container is the space suit, which completely encloses man and, when necessary, through cylinders of compressed oxygen carried on his back, provides the oxygen necessary to keep him alive. The space suit itself is pressurized to an approximation of earth's atmospheric pressure, because at pressures lower than that to be found at an altitude 60,000 feet above the earth's surface, man's body fluids boil and the bubbles in his bloodstream and in his brain kill him.

The other container is the space capsule which, in its simplest form, has been made so well known by the Mercury astronauts, starting with Colonel John Glenn.

Even in its simplest form the Mercury space capsule is not simple at all. It must provide the same controlled pressure that man is accustomed to on the earth's surface; it must provide sufficient oxygen for him to breathe, food for him to eat, water for him to drink. In addition, it must control or dispose of the carbon dioxide he exhales every time he breathes, and the carbon monoxide and other waste products of his body. Further, it must protect him from cosmic radiation coming toward the earth or the astronaut's flight path from the depths of outer space; it must protect him from the radiation which is trapped in the magnetic fields of the earth and some other planets; and it must protect him from man-made nuclear radiation which currently augments the radiation intensity of the earth's Van Allen belts. Further, when nuclear-powered spaceships come into use, it must protect him from the radiation of his own propulsion system.

In addition, of course, there are a great many mechanical complexities which are a part of the space capsule. These provide for navigating the capsule in space, for which such complicated electronic gadgets as horizon scanners and star-fixed orientation equipment are required. The astronaut needs some kind of periscope or other device with which he can see outside his capsule in order to augment the automatic equipment with his own knowledge and skill as a pilot. The capsule must be equipped with an elaborate communications system so that he can talk to his earth base and receive instructions and advice from there. Then there is the "steering" mechanism which comprises a whole series of jet engines, usually powered by compressed gases carried aboard the capsule, with which he can tilt the space capsule up and down, swing it from left to right, roll it around its axis in the direction of travel, or even turn it end over end, as he must do at the time of re-entry into the earth's atmosphere.

In addition, there must be retrorockets for slowing the space capsule as it enters the earth's atmosphere to avoid temperatures of 3,000°–4,000°F. which would otherwise result. The only way to keep this kind of temperature below a point where it would cook the pilot alive is to dissipate the heat by allowing it to melt away some of the space capsule. This process of dissipating heat by allowing it to melt away part of the heated object is called ablation. Ablation requires a heat shield made of plastic or ceramic material which is thick enough so that before it is all melted away the space capsule will have been slowed down by friction with the atmosphere it is entering to a point where heat is no longer a serious problem.

In addition to the specialized devices for controlling the surface heat of the capsule during re-entry, an air-conditioning system must maintain the internal temperature between tolerable limits during voyages of any duration.

Not very different from the familiar Mercury space capsule, only larger, is the Gemini spacecraft, intended to provide for two astronauts in a single capsule.

In the Apollo program, intended to accomplish manned exploration of the moon, the "container" of earth-like environment gets more complicated. The Apollo spacecraft, intended to take three men on a lunar exploration trip, consists of two major parts: the Apollo capsule proper, plus another unit called the Lunar Excursion Module (LEM). The LEM and the Apollo capsule are launched as a unit toward the moon and remain together during the trip to the vicinity of the moon. After a few orbits around the moon to permit observation of lunar landing conditions, two of the three astronauts will leave the Apollo capsule and will enter, through an air lock, the LEM. The LEM will then be detached from the Apollo spacecraft and will descend to the moon, using retrorockets to slow it enough so that it can be landed on the lunar surface. One man will remain in the Apollo capsule orbiting the moon while his two companions descend to the lunar surface. Once upon the surface, the LEM will be able to move about over that surface to investigate its characteristics, reporting back to the orbiting Apollo capsule by radio. The Apollo capsule will relay the information back to earth with its more powerful communications equipment.

Having stayed upon the lunar surface as long as the LEM's supply of oxygen and other environmental and power factors permit, the LEM will blast off from the surface with its own rockets and rejoin the Apollo capsule which the men will re-enter for their return to earth. The Apollo spacecraft, of course, will have rocket power sufficient to bring the three men and itself back to earth, leaving the abandoned LEM in orbit about the moon. Re-entering the earth's atmosphere, retrorockets will be fired; friction of the atmosphere and dissipation of heat with the ablation shield will slow the returning spacecraft to the point where a parachute or other device can be used to ease the capsule back to earth.

All manned United States spacecraft of the Mercury series have been landed in the sea on their return to earth. The Russians claim to have landed theirs on the earth on solid ground. Present plans of the United States call for developing the Edwards Air Force Base in the Mojave Desert of California into a "solid ground" landing and recovery area for some United States spacecraft of the future.

A third kind of future and more elaborate container of earth-like environment will be built in the form of space stations. The earliest of these will probably orbit earth at an altitude of a few hundred miles. Shuttle buses and space taxis will ferry supplies and personnel from earth to the space station. Some spacecraft destined for far planets may even be assembled in a space station, hauled up there piece by piece by space freighters. These space stations will not only provide living quarters for the crews who will man them and the crews of outgoing spacecraft, but will also provide shops for assembly, maintenance, and minor repairs of spacecraft and their complicated mechanical, photoelectric, and electronic components. In addition, they will provide warehousing space for supplies for space missions to be launched from the space station. Further, they will contain their own environment-generating equipment which will provide the oxygen and water that man needs and will probably even provide an artificial gravity to keep him from losing the calcium in his bones and the "tone" of the tissues in his circulatory system. The reasons for building these elaborate space stations are both economic and practical.

Much of the cost of present-day launchings is expended for the tremendous chemical boosters needed to lift a relatively small payload or spacecraft out of the strong gravitational field in the immediate vicinity of the earth. Under present conditions no part of these boosters is recoverable or reusable. With space stations, and recoverable boosters now under development, a relatively large and heavy spacecraft capable of carrying a crew of several men and supplies for an extended journey could be assembled in a space station beyond the immediate pull of the earth's gravity. Launching the planet-bound spacecraft from this vantage point will make it possible to move a great and useful payload or spacecraft on a planetary journey with a much more economical expenditure of power and cost than would be possible if it were attempted to launch the same weight of spacecraft from the earth's surface. Similarly, it may be possible for the returning spacecraft to "dock" at the space station in much the same way that a big seagoing vessel may anchor in deep water rather than enter a shallow harbor. From the anchorage, personnel and sometimes freight are ferried ashore in small boats. Similarly, returning astronauts can be ferried from the space station to earth in space taxis for which the re-entry problem would be much simpler than for a large spacecraft.

All of these kinds of containers—the space suit, the space capsules in one or more designs, the lunar or planetary excursion modules, and the space stations—can supply man with the things he needs to live. To a great degree they can protect man from the hazards of space, even those of encounter with micrometeorites, providing they are not too large, moving at speeds ten to twenty times those of a bullet on earth. These containers of earth environment, at least as presently envisioned, cannot, however, protect man against himself.

In addition to the dangers we have just been describing which man must conquer if he is to explore space, there are additional psychological hazards, including anxiety, disorientation, and the stresses of being isolated for a long period of time from the surroundings in which he has evolved.

A great deal of work is being done in laboratories to attempt to determine how these psychological stresses will affect a man in space. Laboratory experiments are rarely a valid substitute for the real experience; consequently, the final answers to these problems can only come from sending astronauts on extended space trips. One somewhat similar experience which man can encounter on earth is found in the regimes of atomic-powered submarine crews who remain submerged for thirty days or longer at a time. In it there is the same absence of a recognizable normal day-night cycle; there is considerable confinement in a restricted space, and a great deal of isolation from the familiar world. Nevertheless, there are a great many more men in the average submarine crew than there will be, for some time at least, in the average spacecraft crew and, consequently, this gives greater variety to the experience. In addition a 30- or 45-day period of confinement in a submarine cannot be compared to, say, a 2- or 5-year round trip to a planet. Obviously, much work needs to be done in this area.

When we have equipped man mechanically, physically, and psychologically for space trips it is only natural to ask what he will encounter in space. Will there be other beings like ourselves? Will he find new forms of life unimagined on earth?

Other Beings?

When most people ask, "Is there life in space?" they are, of course, thinking of other human beings, or at least some kind of being we would recognize as a thinking being, perhaps even one with a soul.

In short, someone with whom we could communicate; someone we could feel kinship with. Despite man's pride in his uniqueness, he seeks companionship on the cosmic as well as the personal level.

The possibility of other beings like ourselves requires, as the barest minimum, conditions similar to those existing on earth. As we have seen before, these are very special conditions, and they occupy a very narrow span of the spectrum of conditions which can exist on planets in terms of temperature, chemical composition, atmospheric conditions, etc. Also, scientists believe that not all stars have planets. So, to estimate the possibility of the existence of other beings like ourselves, let us first examine the likelihood of other planets similar to our own.

Our sun, our star, is one of 100 billion stars in the Milky Way galaxy. Our galaxy is one of 100 billion galaxies *in that portion of the universe of which we are aware*. Each time we build a better telescope, we find that there are more galaxies beyond the ones we have previously known. Perhaps the universe is truly *infinite!*

Some mathematician has said that if an infinite number of chimpanzees were punching an infinite number of typewriters for an infinite length of time, somewhere in the process they'd turn out a play like Shakespeare's *King Lear*—according to the laws of probability!

According to the same laws of probability, many scientists believe that there must be not one but multitudes of other planets with essentially the same conditions that exist on earth—conditions in which beings like ourselves could evolve and live. The stage of their advancement would depend, in part at least, on the age of the planet they inhabited. They might have arrived at the condition of the Neanderthal man (with whom we could *not* communicate), or that of twentieth century Americans, or so far advanced that they would regard us as being in the Neanderthal category.

The theory having the widest acceptance today on how planets are formed about a star goes something like this: Each star, as part of the great revolving wheel or dish that is the galaxy in which it has its place, is traveling through space at unimaginable thousands of miles per second. The space through which it travels, while it is a better

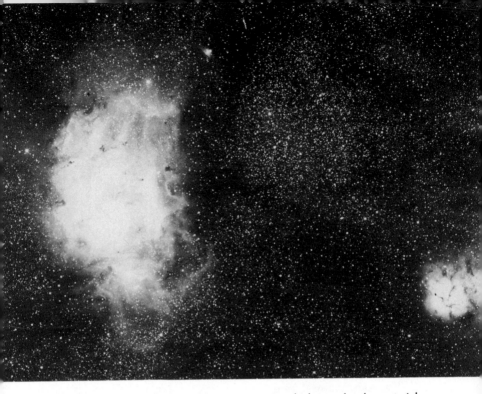

Photo showing the kind of space dust some scientists think may be the material from which planets are made around a star. (*Mount Stromlo Observatory*)

vacuum (by something like a million times) than any we can produce in earthbound laboratories, is nevertheless filled with gas and "space dust." In some places the gas-dust clouds are thicker than in others. When a star wheels through such a relatively dense cloud, it probably picks up—because of its strong gravitational pull—a huge trailing envelope of gas and space dust. Trailing behind the star, this envelope—still because of the star's gravitational pull—tends to clump into even denser clots which thus begin to develop their own gravitational pull, each molecule exerting an attraction on every other molecule in the clot, until the clots form more-or-less solid planets. It may be that a star can pass through more than one of these relatively dense gas clouds in the course of its lifetime. In fact there is some evidence that this has happened in our own solar system. For example, while the earth is quite dense, in fact the densest of the sun's planets, Jupiter, one of the largest, has a density *less than that of water*—if a piece of it could be brought to earth and dropped into the sea, it would float! It is difficult to talk about the "clouds" that seem to surround Jupiter, because they are probably the stuff of which the planet itself is made, only becoming denser as the center of this huge planet is approached. Thus it is conceivable that Jupiter may be the result of a more recent passage of the sun through a dense gas cloud—more recent than that from which the earth and some of the other planets were formed, since they have had time to become more dense, which would be the tendency as their period of rotation slowed and the accumulated gas was pulled in toward the center by molecular attraction—gravity.

Thus planets of a single star can be of greater or lesser age. Similarly, stars are of greater or lesser age. Consequently, any living beings inhabiting the multitudes of planets which could be expected to have conditions supporting life like our own might be in any stage of development from the most primitive to a stage of advanced civilization and personal development which we cannot even imagine.

The most natural thing is to think of other sentient beings as having physical and mental characteristics similar to our own. Much scientific thinking on the problem of life on other planets has been along these lines. Earth life is based on a water-oxygen chemistry. Water forms the basis of the fluids in which life processes take place; oxygen the factor which accomplishes the release of energy (from food) for activity and tissue building.

It is conceivable, however, that other chemical systems could support life. Earth life might be described as a hydrocarbon-nitrogen system, comprising hydrogen, oxygen, carbon, and nitrogen. These four elements make up most of human body tissues.

Another system which seems to offer possibilities is one comprising hydrogen (the most abundant material in the universe), carbon, nitrogen, and a class of substances called halogens. Halogens are a group of chemicals comprising fluorine, chlorine, bromine, and iodine. Of these, chlorine may be the most likely substitute in some other world for the oxygen of this world.

Oxygen is corrosive—that is, it reacts chemically with a great number of other elements to change their characteristics. Chlorine is also corrosive. In addition, both oxygen and chlorine combine with many other elements in what is technically called an exothermic reaction—that is, the combination gives off heat. Heat is a form of energy which can be used to do work—the work of moving, of thinking, of building, and destroying. In other words, the conversion of chemical elements, by chemical processes, into energy is one characteristic of the things we call living beings.

In such a system, it is possible that hydrochloric acid (HCl) might substitute for water as a medium in which many life processes could take place: the forming of tissue compounds, the conversion of "food" into energy, etc. After all, hydrochloric acid is one of the chief constituents of *human* digestive juices! It does not seem too farfetched that it might serve other beings in more ways than it does us.

Both the hydrocarbon-nitrogen system which makes human life possible and the hydrocarbon-nitrogen-halogen system just proposed would function in about the temperature range we are accustomed to on earth, although the latter could probably function in a colder environment than we humans could stand.

If now we consider varying the temperature of the planet upward, even more bizarre possibilities arise. Some of the elements we call metals, that are relatively hard solids at normal earth temperatures, become liquids as the temperature rises above 400° or 500° F., and more metals become liquid around 800° to 900°. Many of these metallic elements combine with other elements to release energy; at appropriate temperatures they are liquids in which energy-releasing and chemical-compound-forming reactions could take place. Who is to say that under these conditions some form of living being could not exist? It is a law of chemistry that for every 10° C. (about 18°F.) rise in temperature, the speed of a chemical reaction doubles. This would suggest that these high-temperature, liquid-metal-type creatures would live very fast. Fast reaction times, tremendous mental capabilities, and perhaps short life spans.

Letting imagination reach even farther afield, another way of describing a human being (we have just reviewed the concept of life as a thermochemical system) would be as an electrochemical system. Certainly all that distinguishes human life from earthly forms of non-life is related to the brain and its associated nervous system. The human nervous system functions largely on electrical and electromagnetic impulses. It is these which make it possible for us to see, smell, feel, move, and think. In the case of humans, the chemical reactions in the nerve and brain tissue are the source of these living electrical impulses, although we do receive some electromagnetic impulses from outside the chemistry of our bodies, as when we perceive light and color or when our moods are subtly influenced by the magnetic field of the earth.

With this understanding of the part that electromagnetic phenomena play in human life, it is not impossible to imagine a form of life on some other planet which was sustained by and acted entirely through electromagnetic fields and pulses of one sort or another.

Before we dismiss this concept as too fantastic let us consider how we know that we are human beings. For example, if there were only one human being on earth, would he know he was a human being? The answer is: No!—because we must react and communicate with other human beings to recognize our humanness. It is through these human contacts that we are aware of our humanity—through them we live! We affect one another—we are affected by others. We are aware of others—they are aware of us.

Some of this awareness and interaction is purely physical, some intellectual, and some emotional. The latter two modes of contact depend largely on the electrical impulses in our nervous systems.

On the physical level, we can walk up to someone and push him. This results in his feeling the push and, if the push is strong enough, it displaces him in space. Instead of pushing, we might say, "Step over there, please!" In most cases, the person spoken to receives a stimulus which he interprets in his electronervous system, sends some electronervous impulses to his legs, and again he is displaced in space.

In comparison, there are eddies or concentrations of energy in electrical and magnetic fields which could be thought of as entities or beings. As they impinge on each other, they are deformed to a greater or less degree; and the impingement of one upon the other (a push) may result in displacing one or both in space. Similarly, they can influence each other in both shape and location in space from a distance. To this degree they are "aware" of each other, they interact with each other, they influence each other. Who is to say that they do not recognize in each other the nature of their own existence? Thus it is conceivable that there may be wholly electromagnetic beings who are completely intellectual or spiritual.

But then there intrudes into this concept the basic physical law that mass is energy and energy is mass, and so perhaps the electromagnetic beings just described are only transient thoughts straying along the nervous system of a physical body so great that we cannot imagine it. There is such a remarkable uniformity in the structures of the universe! Our solar system is so much like a simple atom! A central nucleus, the sun, is surrounded by a few electrons, the planets. Who knows? Our solar system, its planets, including our earth, may be an atom in the boot heel of God!

With the possibility of so many other intelligent beings in the universe, and with the obvious difficulties of traveling outside our own galaxy, the question naturally arises: Why don't we attempt to communicate with beings in other worlds by radio or television? This question has, of course, occurred to many scientists, and some of them are engaged in doing just that: trying to communicate with or at least listen for communications from other worlds.

One such project has had scientists listening to radio "noise" from radio-transmitting sources throughout the nearby universe for the past several years in an attempt to find a recognizable signal. Because there are so many galactic and extragalactic sources of radio noise, the volume of the noise is certain to be higher than the volume of any intelligent signal. Nevertheless, the skill of the electronikers is such that they can "reach below the noise level" to pick out discreet signals. The method of doing this is to screen out all the random noise arising from colliding galaxies, radio stars, and other sources of electromagnetic radiation in the frequencies usually utilized for radio communication on earth. This screening process is accomplished by electronic circuits called discriminators—they can discriminate, on earth, at least, between the "hash" of background noise and a discreet signal. In taking this approach to the problem, of course, we assume that other beings may have the same ideas that we do about what is "hash" and what is "signal."

If we assume that this is true, we are still left with the problem of what code they will use. Even language is a "code" in which we express ideas. So what code are the extraterrestrial beings using? A great deal of thought has been given to this problem, too. Some scientists, for example, assume that mathematics must really be the basic language of any life system advanced enough to want to communicate with others in the universe. Supposedly $2 \times 2 = 4$ anywhere in the universe. On the basis of this assumption they have been particularly listening for—and in at least one experiment have been transmitting—a series of "dots and dashes" or digitized data which to earth men represent some basic mathematical concepts. Listening, listening, listening, transmitting and listening, and to date no recognizable results.

It may simply be that our techniques are not sufficiently refined, or perhaps our understanding is not sufficiently great. In addition to these conceptual lacks which may be hampering us there are some great technical difficulties in the way of communicating with other planets in or out of the solar system. Because these difficulties are related to distance, the farther we point our antennas, the greater the difficulties become.

Men have long thought that Mars was the most likely planet in our solar system to support some kind of life which we might recognize as an intelligent race of beings. At this distance radio communication is not too difficult, for Mars comes within about 30 million miles at its closest approach to earth. Modern technology and our experience with it on Mariner's voyage to Venus show that we can easily communicate great amounts of intelligible information over distances of at least 50 million miles. We know, because with the

Mariner spacecraft we have done it. The one-way transit time for a radio signal to Mars is only about three minutes.

But once we get out of our own solar system, watch out! The nearest star, Alpha Centauri, is approximately four light years away. Since radio waves travel at the same speed as light waves, this means that it would take four years to send a message to a planet associated with our nearest star neighbor. It would also require four years for the return message, if any, to reach earth. This would mean that we could accomplish a complete communication with any possible planet of the star Alpha Centauri only once every eight years. Now, if both parties to this interplanetary communication used and understood the same code or language, this would result in pretty slow exchange of information. If, however, you imagine yourself on earth trying to talk by a sort of sign language that had to be worked out as you go along, with a Piute Indian on an Alpha Centauri planet, you get a clearer idea of what the communication problem is with our *nearest* interstellar neighbor.

The star Alpha Centauri may or may not have inhabited planets associated with it. The reason that scientists think there may be other intelligent life in the universe, is that the billions upon billions of stars, some of which surely have (by the law of averages) inhabitable planets, make the existence of extraterrestrial life likely. But this doesn't mean that our nearest star neighbor is the "sun" of another earth. In fact, our nearest intelligent neighbors could be on a planet associated with a star halfway across the galaxy in which we find ourselves. The Milky Way galaxy of which our sun and its planets are a part, is 120,000 light years across. This means that radio contact with a planet accompanying another star which might be halfway across our own galaxy could take 60,000 years for a one-way message; it would require 120,000 years for the two-way transmission of a complete exchange.

If we were to radio, "Are you there?" and assuming someone was there and understood, the answering "Yes!" would reach earth 120,-000 years later. In the year 121,964 it might be difficult for anyone to remember what question had been asked in 1964! Judging by present conditions, 6,000 generations of earth men would have lived and died between asking the question and getting the answer. One hundred and twenty thousand years ago your ancestors lived in caves

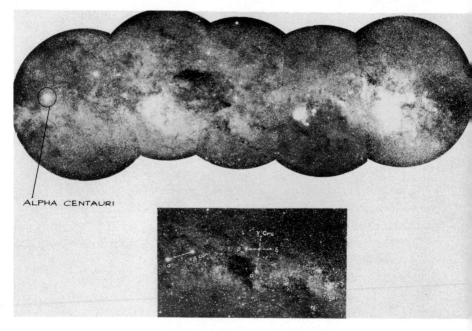

Photos of the southern part of the Milky Way, showing *Alpha Centauri,* our nearest star neighbor. *(Mount Stromlo Observatory)*

and fought with clubs; 120,000 years from now who knows what your descendants will be doing?

Some people will suggest, "Why worry about understanding the language or communications of other beings; why not just send a television camera on a spacecraft to scan at least the *nearby* planets, and possibly, in the future, those planets which may be associated with the nearest star?" This, in fact, is exactly one of the things that scientists are working on. Here, too, we have some problems. Your home television set probably forms the picture you see on the screen by scanning the screen rapidly with an electron beam that makes about 100 lines per inch. If you assume similar picture quality and a picture 4 × 4 inches, this means 400 × 400 lines to a single picture, or (as the scientists call it) 160,000 "bits" of information which must be transmitted from the television camera on the spacecraft to the television viewer on earth.

The number of "bits" of information which can be transmitted per second depends, with present techniques, on the bandwidth of the transmission signal. Home television sets generally use a bandwidth of about 20,000 cycles per second. In a spacecraft, where you are using relatively low power to transmit over long distances, the band-

NGC 5194 spiral nebula in *Canes Venatici*, Messier 51. A galaxy which looks much as the Milky Way would if photographed from the same angle; but it is only about one-third of the 120,000 light-year diameter of the Milky Way. (*Mount Wilson and Palomar Observatories*)

width must be much narrower. The Ranger spacecraft with which we expect to get television pictures of the moon (only 250,000 miles away) will transmit on a bandwidth of only 2,000 cycles per second.

The Mariner spacecraft with which we expect to get television pictures of Mars (30 million miles away) will use a transmission signal with a bandwidth of only 10 cycles per second. So, if you divide the 160,000 "bits" of information required to make up a single 4 × 4-inch picture by 10, you find that it will take 16,000 seconds, or about 4 hours to transmit a single picture. Electromagnetic disturbances in the sea of energy through which this signal must travel from Mars to earth will undoubtedly spoil some parts of the four-hour transmission; it will probably be necessary, therefore, to send the picture over and over again, perhaps ten times, before all the parts are perfect on some one transmission, so that a composite single perfect picture can be made by assembling the "good" parts from all the transmissions.

Scientists also want to include microphones in any spacecraft to be landed on another planet in the hope of picking up the sounds of living things for radio broadcast to earth. These sounds could be the swish of grasses in the Martian breeze, or the astounded chatter of Martians gathered around the unidentified flying object (UFO) just arrived from earth.

If you don't want to wait for the slow progress of the scientists in their efforts to solve the puzzle of extraterrestrial life, you can go to the government-owned Giant Rock Airport near the town of Twenty-Nine Palms in California's vast Mojave Desert on an October week end when the UFO fans have a convention annually attended by 10,000 or more. There you can meet people who are convinced that they have not only witnessed the arrival of spacecraft bearing extraterrestrial beings, but some who have even been taken on trips and had other experiences with the space people. A book written by one of these enthusiasts is titled *My Venusian Lover*.

7. Tools for Space Exploration

Man has been probing space, with his eyes and his mind, at least, since his advent on earth and his first searching look at the sun and the wonders of the night sky. Recorded history shows that the Egyptians, some of their precursors, and some of their contemporaries, as long ago as six thousand years, had a great deal of information about the movement of the planets in the heavens and were using stars by which to navigate on sea and on land.

The first telescope of which we have any record was invented in 1608 by a Dutchman called Hans Lippershey. Galileo, the Italian astronomer, heard about Lippershey's invention and built his first telescope in 1610. With this first crude instrument Galileo made some remarkable discoveries. From that time telescopes have been improved immeasurably and they have been surrounded with auxiliary equipment which helps man understand and analyze the information his telescopes gather. The optical telescope—one which uses light to learn about planets and stars—was man's first important tool for the exploration of space. It continues to be an important tool.

The radio telescope, developed after World War II, uses the radio frequency part of the electromagnetic spectrum with which to learn about distant stars and galaxies. Recently, it has been used in conjunction with optical telescopes to expand the range of the optical scope and to provide additional information about "radio" stars and galaxies which the radio telescope has been able to discover.

For exploration and examination of planets in our solar system, the radar transceiver is a more active, but shorter-range, first cousin to the radio telescope.

The spacecraft described in some of the previous chapters in this book have made it possible to bring other tools into the exploration of space. The spacecraft themselves may be likened to buses which transport certain travelers, called man's experiments or tools for the exploration of space, on a prescribed trip during which the scientific instruments make observations on the environment through which they are passing and, through telemetry, report their findings to earth. These spacecraft bus passengers comprise a new set of tools for exploring space.

Let us look briefly at each of these major categories of tools for the exploration of space and see what they accomplish and how they do it.

How Far Can We See?

The most powerful optical telescope in the world today is the Hale telescope on Mt. Palomar, about halfway between Los Angeles and San Diego, California. This 200-inch reflecting telescope was financed by the Rockefeller Foundation and dedicated on June 3, 1948. It is operated jointly by the California Institute of Technology and the Carnegie Institution of Washington, D.C. This huge 6.5 million-dollar telescope and others of its kind are not telescopes in the sense that a man can "look" through them; they are more truly elaborate and very specialized cameras. One of the amazing things about this 530-ton giant is that it can be controlled so accurately that it will remain focused upon a chosen star, millions of light years away in space, automatically compensating for the rotation of the earth, the movement of the earth in its orbit around the sun, and the travel of the sun in the giant wheel of the Milky Way galaxy.

Another way of describing this giant telescope and others of its kind is that it is a "light accumulator." By keeping its huge reflecting mirror focused on a given star for several hours at a time, the reflected light is accumulated on a very sensitive photographic emulsion to give accurate pictures of stars and other galaxies much too faint to be detected by the most sensitive human eye. The reason for the remarkable ability of this kind of telescope is that the human eye cannot "accumulate" light over a very long period of time—the light that reaches your retina is converted into an electrical impulse leading along your nervous system to your brain almost instantaneously. Because the chemistry of the photographic emulsion is different from the chemistry of your eye, the light falling upon the photographic emulsion can be "accumulated" over a period of several hours, building a stronger and stronger impression the longer the plate is exposed to the light. In this way the fantastic camera which we call a reflecting telescope can "see" things a million times too faint to be detected by the human eye and brain working alone.

One of the most useful adjuncts to the telescope is the spectroscope, a device for separating the incoming light into its component colors or wavelengths. For astronomers and others who wish to probe the secret of space, one of the most useful bits of knowledge which

World's biggest telescope, the 200-inch, on Mount Palomar, halfway between Los Angeles and San Diego, California. (*Mount Wilson and Palomar Observatories*)

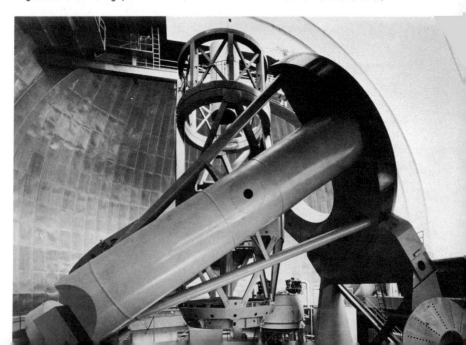

the science of physics has given to man is that each chemical element emits its own characteristic wavelength (color) of light when it is heated to incandescence. Since the stars studied with optical telescopes are all incandescent—light-emitting—the spectroscope makes it possible to tell a great deal about the stars. From the light they emit, analyzed by a spectroscope attached to the telescope, we can determine the chemical composition of a star. By comparing the spectrographic analysis of one star with those of other stars we can also learn something about the star's age.

If we turn the telescope upon nearer heavenly objects such as the planets in our own solar system, a corollary bit of knowledge from the physicist helps us to learn more about the planets. This corollary bit of knowledge is that chemical elements making up the surface of the planet which reflects light, or those chemical elements in its atmosphere, *absorb* certain wavelengths (colors) in the light spectrum. Knowing this, we can use the spectroscope to analyze the light of the sun (full spectrum) reflected from the planet Venus, for example (partial spectrum), and we learn by noting the missing wavelengths of the reflected light what light-absorbing chemical elements make up the surface of the planet and its atmosphere. When the planet is between the earth and the sun we observe the sun's light transmitted through the planet's atmosphere and can then determine what elements make up this atmosphere. By subtracting these from those indicated by the light reflected from the planet *through* its atmosphere we can determine the actual composition of the reflecting surface of the planet.

A reflecting telescope such as that on Mt. Palomar can "see" galaxies and stars at a distance of two billion light years. This means that the light which makes an image of such a distant galaxy on a photographic plate at Mt. Palomar tonight left its source at a time when the universe was only half as old as it is now estimated to be. Because it has taken light so long to travel from these distant galaxies to our telescopes, the galactic events which are recorded on the photographic plates are those which happened as long as two billion years ago; the galaxy from which this light originated may not even be in existence today. All we can be sure of is that two billion years ago the galaxy we photograph tonight looked as it is shown upon the photographic plate.

The physicist has given us another bit of knowledge generally referred to as the Doppler shift. You will remember that the Doppler theory explains why, as a train approaches you, the tone of the whistle seems to rise, and, as the train passes you and recedes into the distance, the tone of the whistle drops again. This well-known sound effect is due to the fact that as the train is rushing toward you the sound waves are crowded together, or given a higher frequency, which makes the tone seem to go up the scale. As the source of the sound recedes, it tends to stretch out the sound waves—lower their frequency—and therefore the tone drops.

The same effect applied to light waves is known as the red shift, and makes it possible to determine the direction and speed relative to earth of some of the nearer stars and galaxies outside our own solar system.

No matter how powerful a telescope, those of the past have always had one serious disadvantage: They were located upon the surface of the earth. Affixing a telescope to the surface of the earth gives it one advantage, that of stability, particularly if it is located upon such a large slab of granite on the earth's crust as Mt. Palomar. But it has a great disadvantage, and that is the fact that it must look through the earth's atmosphere at whatever it directs its gaze in space. While the earth's atmosphere is the source of great protection and benefit to human beings, it is not an ideal medium for the transmission of interstellar light. The problem of the astronomer trying to use an earthbound telescope is not so severe, but is similar to that of a skin diver peering up through five fathoms of water and trying to read the identification markings on a plane flying several thousand feet overhead. Both water and the earth's atmosphere tend to bend the light rays. Because air is a fluid, constantly in motion, it distorts the images which would otherwise reach the emulsion on the telescope's photographic plate with much greater clarity.

In view of these difficulties and the advantages to be gained if the

This three-picture series of a Republic Aviation Corporation F-105F rising off the runway through turbulent into still air is a dramatic illustration of the problems astronomers have in "seeing" through turbulent air near the earth's surface. (*Republic Aviation Corporation*)

A Vee balloon developed by the Goodyear Aerospace Corporation as a relatively stable platform for high altitude optical observatories. (*Goodyear Aerospace Corp.*)

telescope could be mounted beyond most or all of the earth's atmosphere, in several recent experiments telescopes have been borne aloft by balloons to make observations from high above the earth, where the amount of atmosphere the light rays must pass through is only 5 or 10 per cent of that between the space object and the actual surface of the earth.

The difficulty of pointing a balloon-supported telescope at the proper object in the sky and keeping it in focus as the balloon is borne along upon upper-atmosphere winds is not a small one. The use of gyroscopes and air-borne computers to activate aspect-controlling mechanisms has done a lot to solve the problem, and these techniques will probably be further perfected in the future.

An even more ambitious project is the Orbiting Astronomical Observatory (OAO). The OAO will carry aloft a star-gazing telescope mounted on an earth-orbiting satellite. This OAO satellite will be orbited completely beyond earth's atmosphere, and its progress through space will be so uniform and so predictable that the proper focusing of the telescope upon the objects which it is desired to examine will be much simpler than with balloon-supported telescopes. The OAO will probably transmit its findings to earth by a system of communications similar to television transmission.

As a small example of what this kind of observatory may be able to accomplish, let us refer back to the "canals" on Mars. These markings on Mars can be detected by earthbound telescopes only during extremely good "seeing" atmospheric conditions. They have not been photographed because the duration of ideal conditions in the atmosphere between the telescope and Mars has been so short that photography has been impractical. The canals of Mars have been seen fleetingly by trained human observers who have sketched what they saw. When the sketches were compared they showed remarkable agreement. By placing a telescope beyond the earth's atmosphere, the light reaching it from Mars would not be subject to the distortions encountered when the light must travel through the earth's atmosphere; consequently, it should be possible with the OAO to get a clear, sharp picture of the surface features of Mars, with or without canals!

Related to the OAO is a planned Orbiting Solar Observatory (OSO). The telescope of this satellite, of course, will be fixed upon the sun and will make it possible to learn much more about this source of earth's life than has ever been learned before. In this case, too, what the telescope sees will be transmitted to earth by television techniques.

How Far Can We Hear?

The radio telescope, so-called because it observes electronically that portion of the electromagnetic spectrum commonly called radio frequencies, was developed shortly after World War II and has added a lot to the astronomers' knowledge of space and the many objects in it. The radio telescope brings several new capabilities as a space-investigating tool: it can be used day or night, while the optical tele-

A radio-telescope installation used for observing celestial bodies by the amount of radio energy (instead of light energy) which they emit. (*California Institute of Technology*)

scope can be used only on clear nights; it can "see" through clouds as well as atmospheric turbulence; and it can penetrate farther than an optical telescope: 6 billion light-years compared to 2 billion light-years.

This last capability of the radio telescope may be attributable either to the fact that energy in the radio frequencies travels through space more readily than does energy in the frequency of light; or it may be due to the fact that extragalactic sources of radio energy are more powerful than similar sources of light energy.

It is interesting to note that radio sources and light sources are often the same galaxies or the same stars. Early use of radio telescopes resulted in the construction of a "radio map" of the heavens, locating strong radio-frequency sources of energy. Once this information became generally available to astronomers, many of those with optical telescopes trained their instruments on these same places in the heavens and, by using longer photographic exposures, were able to take pictures of galaxies and stars which they had not previously realized existed. In these cases, the radio source also turned out to be a light source, but often a very faint one because of extreme distance or relatively low energy level in the light frequency part of the spectrum.

In construction the radio telescope is like a very sensitive radio receiver using an antenna which can be "tuned" very sharply to certain frequencies and which can be directed, or steered, very precisely in both azimuth and elevation, in much the same manner as the optical telescope.

In early 1964, scientists began testing the biggest radio telescope of them all, near Arecibo, Puerto Rico. Here a natural bowl in the Puerto Rican mountains about 1,000 feet in diameter has been converted into a huge radio antenna by laying steel mesh on the ground to line the inside of this small depression. This antenna is steered, or pointed, by moving the feed-receiving point above the bowl on intersecting cables.

Some of the greatest and most interesting sources of strong radio-frequency signals arise from the collision of two galaxies. The galaxies do not collide in the usual physical sense of one star crashing headlong into another and splattering the heavens with superheated fragments of matter. Instead, the colliding galaxies may pass through each other without one star impinging upon another and without a single planet being dislodged from its appointed orbit. The clash from which the radio signals arise is a clash of magnetic fields and electrostatic plasmas. As the strong electromagnetic fields surround-

This photograph of a group of galaxies in *Perseus*, a strong radio source, was taken with an optical telescope. Some radio sources are dark clouds of gas which do not show up on an optical scope except as shadowy forms between the telescope and some more distant light-emitting object. (*Mount Wilson and Palomar Observatories*)

ing the individual stars and the galaxies cross each others' paths they give rise to tremendous outpourings of energy in the radio-frequency portion of the electromagnetic spectrum. This energy causes signals so strong that they cross billions of light-years of space to be detected by earth-borne antennas and elaborate electronic receivers.

The distances between the stars in a given galaxy are so vast that one galaxy may pass completely through another without any of the stars touching or coming close enough to disturb their planets in their appointed paths. The galaxies, too, are so huge that for one to pass through another may take 200 million years or longer, and this at speeds of thousands of miles per second.

In addition to discovering sources of radio energy which are also sources of light energy and thus working in conjunction with optical telescopes, the radio telescopes have found so-called black stars or dark clouds of gas in the universe which emit radio energy but no light energy. In this way they are adding vastly to our knowledge of the natural travelers in the sea of space beyond what optical telescopes can tell us.

How Far Can We "Look"?

An active and younger cousin of the radio telescope might be called the radar telescope. In the radio telescope, the technique is to listen "passively" for radio frequency signals originating in space, receive them, and analyze them to learn what we can about their source. In the radar telescope, the signal is transmitted from the earth to be bounced off a heavenly body and received back on earth. The received signal is then analyzed in many of the same ways and some new ways to determine the nature of the object off which the radar signal was bounced.

This work has been pioneered by Robertson Stevens and Walter Victor of the JPL. Starting by bouncing radar signals off the moon, following this with radio transmission of music and a message by President Eisenhower which was bounced off the moon and received here on earth, this group has gone on to radar examination of the surface features of Venus, Mars, and recently, Mercury.

Radar examination of objects in space requires tremendous amounts of power and extremely sensitive receiving apparatus because of the great loss inherent in this kind of transmission. For example, in a recent radar contact with the planet Mercury, the signal transmitted from the 85-foot antenna at Goldstone, California, was the equivalent of approximately 50 million watts of power; the signal received back from Mercury was about one 10 billion billionth watt of power. This means, for the present at least, that radar examination of planets will be confined to those close to us in the solar system. Even those "close" to us are examined at distances of 40 to 50 million miles.

A study of the returning signals from radar transmission can tell the radar astronomers some interesting things. One very important thing they learn is the exact distance between the earth and a given planet under study. If you are planning to send a spacecraft to Venus, it is important that the distances to planets and the shape of their orbits around the sun be determined accurately. Radar sometimes makes possible the determination of these distances within a few hundred feet.

By using the Doppler effect—the phenomenon which makes the whistle of an approaching train sound higher than the same whistle as it passes and departs from you—the radar astronomer can determine the angular speed, or speed in its orbit, of a planet in relation to the sun and to the earth. Precise knowledge of the speed is also important in establishing spacecraft trajectories directed toward the planet.

By examining the characteristics of the return signal it is also possible to determine the rate of rotation of a planet—how fast it is turning upon its axis. The roughness of the planet's surface and the composition of the surface (how good a radar reflector it is) may also be determined from an examination of the returned radar signal.

A specific example of this type of space exploration is the Venus radar study of 1961 and 1962.

Venus Radar Experiments

At the Goldstone complex of the Deep-Space Tracking Net, in addition to the Pioneer site which is intended for the reception of information telemetered from spacecraft and for the tracking of spacecraft, there is an Echo site and a Venus site, the latter designed for radar astronomy and communications research.

In 1961, the Venus site was used successfully to bounce radar signals off the planet Venus, the return signal being received after six and a half minutes during which it had traveled the 70 million-mile round trip.

Actually, the experiments used both the Echo and Venus antennas, one transmitting 13 kilowatts of power at 2,388 megacycles while the other received the return signal. One purpose, and perhaps the most important, of these experiments is to determine more accurately the astronomical unit, which is the mean distance from the earth to the sun. As a result of these experiments the unit was refined to a value of 92,956,200 miles, plus or minus 300.

Fifty years ago the astronomical unit as plotted by the best optical methods then available was believed to be accurate only to within 250,000 miles. Recently, but before the introduction of the radar astronomy techniques practiced at Goldstone, astronomers believed the astronomical unit to be known to within 60,000 miles. For planetary exploration and close fly-bys, such as the Mariner mission to Venus, an inaccuracy of 60,000 miles could not be tolerated. The distance from the planet Venus at which Mariner's instruments could operate effectively ranged from 8,000 miles from the planet to 40,000 miles from the planet; thus, a 60,000-mile inaccuracy in the distance to the planet or of the planet from the sun might put a spacecraft such as the Mariner far out of effective operating range at the time of the Venus fly-by.

Radar astronomy techniques are quite similar to techniques employing radar on earth to determine the distance to a target in directing gunfire or missiles. The radar signal leaves the transmitter at the speed of light (186,000 miles per second), strikes the target object, and bounces back to the transceiver at the same rate of speed. The time required for the trip is carefully measured in millionths of a second. From this measurement of time, the accurate distance to the target is computed. The same principles apply in determining the distance to the moon or a planet: the time of round-trip travel is interpreted in terms of distance to the object.

Radar investigation of Venus also gave an indication that Venus rotates at a very slow rate, possibly keeping the same face toward the sun at all times. Another interesting factor learned from this radar investigation was that the reflection coefficient of Venus was established at approximately 12 per cent; this is a relatively bright value, close to that of earth, and in contrast to the moon's low 2 per cent reflectivity.

The average dielectric constant of the material making up the surface of Venus was determined by these radar experiments to approximate that of sand or dust. Further, the scattering effect on the reflected radar signal was about the same as that of the moon on an equivalent radar signal, thus indicating that the Venusian surface was quite likely similar to the rocky and cratered surface of the moon.

One as yet unexplained peculiarity revealed by the radar investigation of Venus was the apparent progression of a bright radar spot across Venus from the center toward the outside edge. What feature of the Venusian terrain causes this bright radar spot is yet unresolved, but the direction of its motion seems to indicate that Venus rotates in a direction opposite to its motion in orbit around the sun.

In conjunction with the Mariner mission to Venus in the fall of 1962, the Venus radar experiments were repeated at the Goldstone complex. The results generally confirmed and supplemented the findings of the Mariner II spacecraft on its fly-by of Venus.

Using the same Goldstone equipment, studies of the planet Mercury were conducted by the JPL from May 6 through May 29, 1963. Mercury is the planet closest to the sun and revolves around it once every 88 days; this orbit and the earth's 365-day trip around the sun, makes Mercury available for radar study once every four months. It is a difficult planet to examine because it is so small—only about

3,000 miles in diameter, approximately the same size as the earth's moon. The recently conducted studies of Mercury show that its surface is rougher than either the moon or Venus and that its rotation rate appears to be once every 88 days; thus it always keeps the same face toward the sun.

Closeups!

The tools just described for probing space are what might be termed "long-range" tools. Telescopes, of course, are recognizably long-range instruments. Those carried aboard spacecraft, which we are about to consider, might be likened to microscopes, which are easily recognized as closeup instruments. The spacecraft is a vehicle which carries these instruments directly into the area it is desired to investigate.

When you start talking about spacecraft it is important to make a differentiation between manned and unmanned craft. There are many arguments among scientists about the necessity for putting man in a spacecraft and sending him to the moon or a distant planet. Some scientists contend that an equal amount, or perhaps even a greater amount, of information can be acquired by loading the spacecraft with carefully devised instruments. Generally they feel that perhaps a dozen or more such instruments whose total weight would not equal that of a man would probably produce more information than would be gained from an astronaut.

The only place this argument falls down is when you consider the evaluation of information recorded by instruments, even though it is interpreted by experts, in contrast to the superior capability of a trained human observer to make on-the-spot judgments and adjustments while piloting the craft.

On completely instrumented spacecraft—that do not carry a human pilot—some of the astronauts' functions are taken over by a computer which rides in the spacecraft and turns on each instrument in its turn, accepts its output or observes its response to the environment, perhaps stores this information in its memory (at least temporarily), and then rebroadcasts it to an earth receiving station at the proper time. Scientists on earth usually design the spacecraft so they can "override" the programmed routine.

The reason for this overriding control is that most of the instruments, through the onboard computer, monitor their own performance, so that if something unusual occurs it is reported to earth for a human decision. In this way, the scientists hope to supplement the "intelligence" of the onboard computer with their own intelligence in guiding the process of the investigation.

There are a number of fallacies in this approach, however. One of the difficulties arises from the fact that basically most of the instruments aboard the spacecraft are optical, and those that are not produce for the scientist's observation optical indications. Consequently, the scientist who relies on this approach is limited largely to the sense of sight to tell him what is going on. Lacking are the sense of smell, taste, touch, and hearing; in addition there are many other senses, or at least sensations, associated with our five senses which we do not ordinarily think of but which in new environments are quite important. For example, we do not ordinarily think of our response to the sense of gravity, which holds us on the earth; our sense of inertia, which tells us when we are turning a sharp corner or pulling out of a steep dive; our sense of balance, which tells us when we are being tilted or otherwise jostled in our appointed course. Further, there are eerie responses to the subtle tugs of gravitational and electrical ionized fields which a well-trained human could recognize in a foreign environment.

Of course, man can also build instruments to measure all these things—some of them more accurately than man can perceive them. The problem, of course, is that you do not know which one of all the myriad possibilities you are going to encounter on a given voyage and you cannot put every conceivable instrument into a spacecraft because then you will exceed the weight of a 175-pound man.

Somebody once put the whole matter very succinctly: "Where can you get for 175 pounds a computer anywhere near as good as the human brain?" The statement went on to explain that a computer with the capability of a human brain would occupy a space roughly the size of the Empire State Building (and would weigh almost as much) and would require a flow of water equivalent to Niagara Falls to keep it cool enough to operate. In spite of the fact that computer technology has improved immeasurably since the days in which the statement was made, the comparison is still roughly valid. Under these conditions it is obviously better to send a 175-pound man into space than the kind of computer that could approximate his performance.

The other area in which man can far surpass instruments is in piloting the spacecraft. This capability is due not only to his better-than-computer capability to analyze situations as they arise and to deal with the unexpected, but to the fact that he can *see* what is going on and react to it now! In spite of the fact that most instruments on an instrumented spacecraft provide visual-type information to their masters on earth, the rate of transmission of this information is infinitely slow compared to the pilot's instantaneous visual grasp of a situation that he can bring before the scrutiny of his eyes. The example given a few pages back of how difficult it is to transmit even the 4×4-inch television picture from a distance such as that between Mars and earth, requiring four hours' transmission time for an "imperfect" look at the situation, is in dramatic contrast to the pilot's ability to evaluate almost instantaneously what he can see in one quick glance around him from an astrodome in a spacecraft. Once the pilot has taken his quick look around, he does not have to wait ten or eleven seconds while his information is transmitted to earth, perhaps an hour more while the scientists try to figure out what he meant and make up their minds what to do about it, and another ten or eleven seconds for the message to get back to him. A trained test pilot could act instantly in any situation that he could see or that his instruments reported to him. When you think of the fact that the spacecraft he is piloting may be traveling somewhere between 18,000 and 100,000 miles per second, it is easy to understand that the response to navigational situations will be of the utmost importance.

This does not mean that spacecraft carrying only instruments do not have a place in exploring space—they decidedly do! Particularly until the time we develop much more powerful boosters than we have in the year 1964, the instrumented spacecraft has an advantage in weight, if nothing else. Although the pilot may weigh only 175 pounds, the amount of equipment that is required to take his environment with him weighs a great deal more than this; instruments presently in use do not require earth-like environment. Instead, they have been designed to operate more or less effectively in the harsh environment of space. This means that the weight available on the spacecraft can be used for instruments which will find out things about the space environment instead of devices to maintain an earth-like environment.

You can see from the foregoing that one of the chief functions of these instruments is to find out exactly what the space environment is, so that we can take the necessary measures to protect earth man against it, and to preserve his health and capability to do all the wonderful things out in space that he can do better than instruments. But before we can protect him adequately and can give him the kinds of supporting equipment he needs, we must have detailed information on exactly what kind of environment he is going to encounter.

We need to know how much radiation he needs to be shielded against and what kind of radiation it is. We need to test out with instruments and mechanical equipment different kinds of shielding materials and configurations to determine what is the most effective for the least weight and volume.

If we are going to land on a planet's surface and hope to travel over that surface, we need detailed information on what the surface is like. For example, taking extremes, if the deserts of Mars are like the deserts on earth a capsule maintaining the pilot in an earth-like environment and mounted on something that would look like a simple California dunes buggy would be adequate for traveling around the Martian terrain—at least for the first excursion or two. After this, the observations of the human pilot would enable us to design better and more efficient equipment.

On the other hand, if the surface of the moon is forty feet deep in a dust-like fine powder, this would take an entirely different kind of a vehicle to navigate and explore the terrain.

Specific facts of this nature are things that we can learn from instrumented spacecraft which will carry with them the tools necessary for determining these things. Equally, we will need to know much about the atmosphere on the planet we intend to visit. As a simple case in point, a manned excursion module to wander around the Martian deserts could use the familiar paddle-like solar panels to derive enough energy to operate its instruments, to transmit and receive information from earth, and perhaps even to power the vehicle, *unless* the winds in Martian atmosphere are of such high velocity that they would destroy the paddles or blow over the excursion module which carried them. In the case of existing high winds, the solar panels would have to be affixed to the surface of the vehicle unless, of course, the dust storm stirred up by the winds so darkened the sky that not enough sunlight got through to provide sufficient electrical energy to perform the desired function.

From these simple examples, it can be seen that the problem of learning what the extraterrestrial environment on other planets is like and how to cope with it is a very complicated problem. It needs to be investigated very carefully by instrumented spacecraft before man ventures into these areas.

With this understanding of the problem, let us turn our attention now to the actual tools for this kind of investigation—the "space microscopes," if you will.

The instruments that man will take along in a manned planetary mission will be determined largely by what the instruments on unmanned planetary missions reveal about the nature of the environment and the problems to be encountered there. For this reason, we will not be able to select the necessary equipment until we have conducted several successful unmanned planetary missions. For the unmanned planetary missions, however, plans are pretty specific and equipment is actually under development or, in some cases, completed for instrumenting the unmanned spacecraft. These tools for space exploration we will now briefly review.

When considering what to examine in space, naturally one of the most important things is the nature of the sea of energy, itself, which forms space. The sea of energy, as you will remember, is made up of radiations of one kind or another and of charged particles. It is difficult in some cases to distinguish between radiation and charged particles, for the behavior and the effects of these two phenomena are quite similar, particularly, if you will remember, since the basis of physical laws is the concept of matter as energy and energy as matter.

One of the instruments used in this investigation is called a high-energy charged-particle detector. This device measures primarily cosmic rays, which are essentially the protons or nuclei of hydrogen atoms; it also measures what are called alpha particles, which are the nuclei of helium atoms; further, it measures the nuclei of other heavier atoms and free electrons carrying high electrical charges. A study of the occurrence and behavior of these particles in space, and those trapped in the magnetic field of any planet, is made in the hope of achieving a better understanding of the dynamics of the solar system. Even more significantly for manned space flights, this type of study measures the posibility of radiation hazards to men making extended space flights.

The device itself comprises an ionization chamber and a detector which measures what is called "particle flux": velocity (or energy) of particles times the number of particles. In a spacecraft like the Mariner II, for example, which made a fly-by of Venus in 1962, this high-energy particle detector is contained in a small $6 \times 6 \times 2$-inch box weighing slightly less than three pounds. The box is attached halfway up the spacecraft's superstructure to isolate it as much as possible from secondary-emission particles produced when cosmic rays strike the structure of the spacecraft itself. Such a high-energy particle detector must also be located in a place which prevents the structure of the spacecraft from blocking the high-energy radiation from space which it is intended to measure.

The ionization chamber of this unit is a stainless-steel cylinder five inches in diameter, having a wall thickness of only 1/100 of an inch

The cylinder is charged with argon gas surrounding a quartz fiber next to a quartz rod; at launch, both the fiber and the rod have the same electrical potential. When a charged particle enters the chamber, it ionizes some of the argon gas molecules as it passes through. The negative ions accumulate on the rod, thus producing a static electrical charge; the presence of the charge causes the quartz fiber to be attracted to the rod. When it touches the rod, it "closes the circuit" and produces an electrical pulse which is amplified and transmitted to the earth. The frequency of this pulse tells observers on the earth a great deal about the concentration of highly charged particles in space. The charged particles measured by this device have high energy indeed: To penetrate the 1/100th inch stainless-steel wall of the chamber, protons must have a charge of 10 million electron volts (10 MEV), alpha particles a charge of 40 MEV, and electrons a charge of 0.5 MEV.

The flux detector in this high-energy particle measuring device comprises three Geiger-Müller tubes (the heart of Geiger counters). Two of these Geiger-Müller tubes supplement the work of the ionization chamber just described. Each of these two tubes generates a pulse of electrical current whenever a charged particle enters it—like the clicking of a Geiger counter. The purpose of having two tubes is to determine the proportion of different types of charged particles occurring in space. To accomplish this, one tube is shielded by a stainless steel sleeve 8/1000 of an inch thick; and the other is shielded by a sleeve three times that thick and made of electron-stopping beryllium. By comparing the readings of the two tubes the proportion of protons among the charged particles can be determined.

The third Geiger-Müller tube in this assembly has a mica window at one end which admits protons with energies greater than 0.5 MEV and electrons charged at more than 0.04 MEV. Exclusive of the mica window, a magnesium shield covers the rest of the tube and, since the spacecraft carrying the instrument is stabilized in its relation to the sun, it is possible to determine the direction of particles penetrating the window. The end-window through which these particles can enter the third Geiger-Müller tube is inclined 70° from the space-craft-sun line to shield it from direct solar exposure.

Another most interesting feature of space to be examined by these closeup instruments, of course, is that of magnetic fields associated with planets, the sun, or those existing independently in space. To measure magnetic fields, a device called the magnetometer is used. The magnetometer measures magnetic fields in units called gammas. One gamma is equal to about 1/30,000 of the earth's magnetic field. To get an idea of how small a magnetic field this is, the nails in one of your shoes can be expected to produce a magnetic field of one gamma at a distance of approximately four feet.

Since magnetic fields have a directional flow as well as a (changing) shape, it is necessary that the magnetometer have three sensors aligned along three axes which are perpendicular to each other as the three edges of a cube would be where they meet at one corner.

The sensor itself is a coil of wire, or rather it is two coils of wire somewhat like those in a small transformer, with a primary and secondary winding. As the instrument passes through a magnetic field, any change in that field alters the current in the secondary winding in proportion to the strength of the field through which the instrument is passing. By plotting this information for all three sensors as a spacecraft moves through space, a picture of the magnetic field through which the spacecraft is traveling may be constructed.

On a seagoing ship it is necessary to "compensate" a magnetic compass so that it will point to true north in spite of the magnetic fields arising on the ship itself from the presence of electric motors or even the steel hull of the ship. In a similar way, some of the electrical equipment on a spacecraft sets up magnetic fields and the magnetometer must be protected from these or "compensated" for their influence by winding an auxiliary coil of wire around each of the three censors of the magnetometer. For this reason, the magnetometer is one of the last instruments to be mounted on a spacecraft. After the spacecraft is otherwise assembled and ready to go, its permanent magnetic fields are carefully measured and the compensating coils are applied on the magnetometer so that it will measure only the magnetic fields in space without regard to those on the spacecraft which carries it.

Before man visits any planet, even before he attempts to land an unmanned mechanized device on a planet's surface, he needs to know something about the structure of that surface, the nature of the atmosphere, the approximate temperature, etc.

One way of learning something about all these features of our celestial neighbors is to measure the radiation reflected from them; we know the content of the light and to some degree the other magnetic radiation which reaches each planet from the sun. Consequently, by measuring that part of the total sun's radiation which is reflected by the planet's atmosphere and surface we can learn something about the planet itself. A device used for this kind of measurement is called a microwave radiometer. One kind of microwave radiometer, similar to that used on Mariner II to scan the planet of Venus, measures the amount of radiation being reflected from the planet in two wavelengths: 13.5 and 19 millimeters. This is equivalent to approximately 22,222 and 15,789 megacycles per second. The electronic expert or the ham radio operator will recognize these frequencies.

The microwave radiometer comprises a parabolic antenna, in this case 19 inches in diameter, which is mounted on the spacecraft's structure in such a way that it can swing back and forth through a 120-degree scanning arc. The antenna is equipped with a device called a diplexer, which permits it to receive both wavelengths simultaneously without their interfering with each other.

Since the purpose is to determine the amount of radiation reflected from the planet itself, it is necessary to measure the amount of radiation at these two wavelengths which exist in space and which reach the planet from the sun. To accomplish this, two "horn-type" antennas, one for each wavelength, are mounted in such a way as to point away from the parabolic antenna and look into deep space, each measuring the amount of radiation reaching the planet at its particular wavelength. The parabolic antenna's job, then, is to measure the amounts of these two wavelengths which are being reflected from the planet. The difference in values between the "reference horn" radiation levels and those measured by the parabolic antenna will not only tell how much radiation the planet is reflecting in these two frequencies, but it will also tell how much radiation the planet is *absorbing* in these two frequencies. From this kind of information much can be deduced about the composition of the surface of the planet, its temperature, and the composition of its atmosphere.

A device that often accompanies the use of the microwave radiometer is called an infrared radiometer. The infrared radiometer is usually mounted in such a way as to look at the same area of the planet as the microwave radiometer, but the infrared radiometer is an optical device which can detect light emissions in the 8- to 9- and the 10- to 10.8-micron regions of the spectrum, somewhat below the wavelengths of visible red light. The infrared radiometer, like the microwave radiometer, compares the radiation reflected from the planet with that reaching the planet from outer space. By choosing the proper micron wavelength which the infrared radiometer can receive, it is possible to examine the atmosphere of a planet for specific components, such as water vapor or carbon dioxide. This is accomplished—in the case of water vapor, for example—by choosing one wavelength which is known (by earth-bound experiments) *not* to be absorbed by water vapor and another that is known to *be* absorbed by water vapor. By comparing the readings from the two infrared radiometer frequencies, it is possible to determine how much water vapor there is in the atmosphere of the planet being investigated by a spacecraft on a fly-by mission.

The reason that earth scientists are so interested in water, of course, is that it forms the essential element in all life as it is known on earth. Consequently, a measure of the amount of water vapor in the atmosphere of another planet is some indication as to whether or not it is possible there may be life forms somewhat similar to those known on earth.

One of the most fascinating instruments, or tools for space exploration, which can be carried on spacecraft is the high-resolution television camera, which can take closeup pictures of another planet and televise them to earth.

A Vidicon camera of the type to be carried by spacecraft for televising pictures of the moon and perhaps Mars to earth. (*Jet Propulsion Laboratory*)

One which is used on the Ranger series of spacecraft to explore the moon will start taking pictures of the lunar surface when it is still approximately 2,400 miles away from the moon (the moon is approximately 250,000 miles away from the earth). It will continue to transmit these pictures back to the earth as the spacecraft approaches to within about 12 or 14 miles of the moon. While this may not seem really close, the Vidicon camera planned for this use is to be a telescopic type so that the pictures will seem to have been taken from much closer than these figures indicate. In photographic terms, the last full picture televised from this satellite as the spacecraft approaches a crash landing on the moon will have a resolution of about nine feet per single TV line. Since the approach to the moon is planned for a time and location on the moon's surface where the sun's rays will be inclined by from 20 to 70 degrees from the vertical, that portion of the moon's landscape viewed by the Vidicon camera will show sufficient shadows to provide a good idea of the roughness of the terrain.

At least the first trip of such a vidicon camera to the moon will end in disaster for the camera, for it is intended that the spacecraft will crash on the moon's surface, taking pictures as it approaches the point of impact.

Subsequent and more sophisticated spacecraft will make a soft landing on the moon in a way which should not destroy the Vidicon camera; in this case the camera will be so mounted that it can scan the lunar landscape after the spacecraft has landed. These television pictures, too, will be transmitted to earth.

Because it is so difficult to transmit good TV pictures over such great distances, a computer specially designed for the purpose, will accept the televised picture as digital data, clean up the "snow" or "grass" and ghost images, remove geometric distortions (vertical and horizontal alignment), improve the contrast, detect and remove overlapping of images, and generally improve the televised picture. As the computer acomplishes this for a single scan of the vidicon tube over the terrain, it will store the results and then go on to the next photo. When the resulting magnetic tape is "played back" over a television receiving device, the pictures of the moon will appear on the screen in full clarity and without interruption. It should be much like watching a "taped" television show with all the goofs of the actors and most of the troubles of the equipment eliminated. Two or more Vidicon cameras, of course, can provide a stereo picture of the moon from which actual measurements of mountain heights and such other topographic features can be made, just as in the aerial mapping of the earth's surface.

When you begin to consider landing spacecraft on the surface of the moon or other planets, then the "microscopic" concept of tools for exploration of space becomes more real: At least instruments of this type are needed for the close examination of the surface you want to investigate.

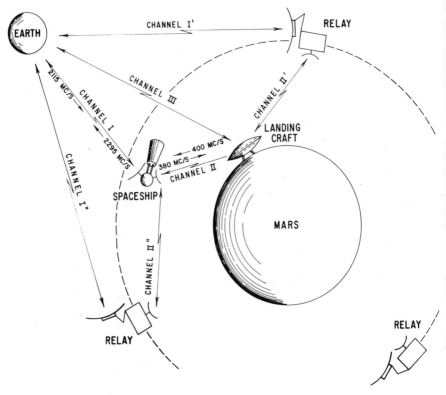

A schematic of a system for televising and telemetering pictures and other data to earth from a rotating planet such as Mars. (*Jet Propulsion Laboratory*)

One of the early things we want to learn about the moon, and about planets other than earth, is something about their internal composition, and this is determined by an instrument called the seismograph. Plans for seismographic studies of other heavenly bodies include the idea of drilling a hole anywhere from one and a half to five feet deep in the surface of the planet. The hole will be big enough to permit the insertion of a one-inch diameter probe. Once the hole is drilled, the probe is inserted and begins to record on sensitive electronic devices the quivers and twitches of the planetary terrain. Because these motions are recorded electronically, they produce electric signals which can be transmitted to earth by telemetry.

At first glance it might seem that the simplest way to drill a hole is by boring one with a revolving bit something similar to the way we drill oil wells on earth. This technique, however, requires more power on a continuous basis than the spacecraft visiting other celestial bodies is liable to have available for this purpose. Most scientists think that the hole can be drilled more easily by repeated impact. Part of the basis for this reasoning is the fact that intermittent demands on an electric power source, at least for the kinds of batteries presently available, are less draining than a continuous demand. For this reason, the probe itself may be sheathed in a sharp-pointed, hard case which will be "pounded" into the ground by a hammer-like weight which is alternately lifted and dropped by electric power from the landing spacecraft.

Another thing that we want to know about the surface of any planet or moon on which we intend to land is how hard and how dense it is. To determine this, there is another little gadget which drops a series of weights with points of various sharpness from a predetermined height (from six to eighteen inches) onto the surface of the planet being investigated. These weights are connected electronically to a device which measures how much time (in thousandths of a second) elapses between the moment of impact and the instant at which the pointed weight stops moving. These millisecond deceleration times, telemetered to earth, will let us know the density of the surface being investigated.

If the spacecraft is capable of movement over the surface of a celestial body, as in the LEM, planned for early moon shots, it will be possible for it to implant instruments called geophones in a predetermined geometric pattern on the surface of the planet. Having done this, the spacecraft will return to some pre-established location, per-

Artist's conception of a landing on the lunar surface. (NASA *photo*)

haps in the center of the pattern it has laid out, to listen while a series of explosions of various strengths are set off by it. The recording of the arrival times, strength, and wave shapes of the signals reaching the listening spacecraft through the structure of the planet will tell a great deal about its subsurface structure and origin. This process is very similar to that by which seismic explorations for oil deposits are made on earth. In fact, it is conceivable, of course, that we may find an undeveloped oil field on the surface of Mars by this process.

The other techniques for measuring the density of the surface and other characteristics of the structures of planets to be visited are almost too numerous to mention and are only limited by the imagination of scientists, who have a great variety of techniques available to them.

Of course it is also desirable to know the chemical constitution of the surface of a given planet, and this can be done by devices which drill out small samples of the surface and make chemical analyses on the spot, the results of which are telemetered back to earth.

But of all the variety of tricks in the scientist's bag, one of the most bizarre is called the "sticky string" technique for determining if there is living matter on a planet.

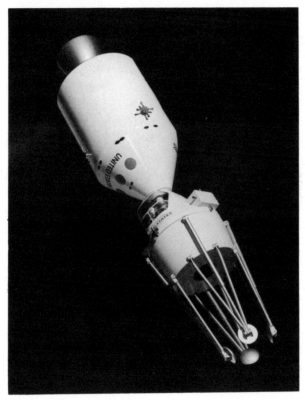

The Apollo Lunar Excursion Module, LEM, as it will appear in orbit around the moon before separation from the orbiting spacecraft for descent to the lunar surface. (*North American Aviation, Inc.*)

In this experiment an actual sticky string is ejected from the landed spacecraft, once it has come to rest upon the surface of the planet. The sticky string is then mechanically drawn back into the box which houses the rest of its instrumentation. When the sticky string comes back into the box it is drawn into a bath of what is called nutrient—a material which would support any kind of low-level life known on earth such as algae, plant spores, bacteria, or viruses.

If, say, Martian bacteria stuck to the sticky string and were drawn into the bath of nutrient, they would begin to grow, multiply, and carry on their life processes.

The trick in this whole system is that the carbon atoms in this nutrient bath were made radioactive before they were sent from earth. Since all life as we know it either gives off or absorbs carbon dioxide, a device like a Geiger counter placed above the nutrient bath can measure changes in the carbon dioxide content of the "atmosphere" entrapped above the nutrient bath. Thus if the sticky string draws into its trap some form of life which gives off carbon dioxide in its life processes, the concentration of radioactive carbon in the atmosphere above the nutrient bath will increase—and instruments will measure this in the same way that a Geiger counter clicks more rapidly when it is brought near a deposit of uranium.

On the other hand, if the particular living organism drawn into the trap absorbs carbon dioxide in its life process, the concentration of radioactive carbon in the atmosphere above the nutrient bath will decrease, the "clicks" of the Geiger counter-type instrument will slow down, and this information will be transmitted to earth for the edification of earth-bound scientists.

One of the newest and, at this moment, most exotic tools for exploration of space is called the laser, standing for light amplification by stimulated emission of radiation. This remarkable device shows so many possibilities, including that of being the "ray gun" or "death ray" of the Buck Rogers comics, that its capabilities can be only begun to be understood. Essentially it is a device for producing a beam of light so intense that it can burn a hole through steel and can be focused so precisely and used so delicately that it may prove an invaluable tool in operations on the brain and eye in human beings.

The laser is essentially a ruby rod with a mirror at one end and a partially transmitting mirror at the other. The nature of the synthetic ruby crystals out of which this rod is made is such that light entering it is bounced back and forth between the two mirrors; on each trip it is given a boost by an electrical impulse until it develops enough energy to pass out of the tube through the end formed by the par-

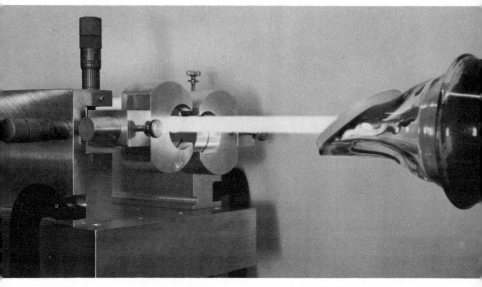

An experimental laser ray-gun showing the beam of coherent light. (*Jet Propulsion Laboratory*)

tially transmitting mirror. At the same time, the nature of the crystal keeps the light from escaping out the sides of the tube.

The significant thing about light generated and energized in this way is that it is what is called coherent light. This means that all the energy is at a single frequency and traveling on a single wavelength.

Ordinary light, such as that from the sun or household light bulbs, is incoherent light; that is, it contains many wavelengths of light vibrating in all possible planes around the direction of travel. In addition, it does not have the kind of energy that can be imparted to light by bouncing it back and forth in the laser tube.

The light produced by the laser is so intense that it can illuminate the moon at a distance of 250,000 miles. Because it is "coherent," it can be directed into such a narrow beam that in transit from the earth to the moon the beam width will spread less than one second of an arc.

The reason that ordinary, noncoherent light loses energy so rapidly in transmission over great distances is that it fans out in all directions, losing energy at a rate proportional to the square of the distance. This means that if you are ten feet from a light source and are receiving light energy at a level of 10,000 lumens and then move twenty feet from the light source, you will receive only 2,500 lumens, or one-fourth as much light.

By providing from its synthetic ruby crystal tube a source of light which is all of the same wavelength and frequency and is directed in a narrow beam, the laser is able to deliver to some distant object a much greater part of its original output.

Some scientists believe, too, that the beams of light from a laser can act in the same way as a radio carrier wave upon which many message signals may be transmitted from one location to another. The chief difference, however, is that the laser beam is capable of carrying infinitely more signals than the radio beam. Since the light in the laser beam moves at the same speed as radio signals (186,000 miles per second), the laser may find great employment in communications of the future, replacing on earth complex overseas cables and coaxial cable television channels. The laser beam, however, is like any other light in that it does not easily go around corners. For this reason we may need to use satellites high in the heavens to receive, amplify, and rebroadcast the laser signal to another point on earth beyond the horizon.

In space exploration, in addition to their high potential as devices for communication, laser beams can be used to drill deep holes in the surface of any visited planet for geophysical and other scientific experiments, or to analyze the chemical content of the surface or subsurface of other planets. And if—heaven forbid—we should encounter hostile beings on another planet, the laser might turn out to be a most effective and lightweight weapon with which to defend ourselves.

One of the hazards which are of great concern to those planning manned exploration of space is the presence of meteorites and micrometeorites in space. These small particles of matter, rock, or iron and nickel, travel through space at speeds of many thousands of miles per hour. They have a velocity ten to twenty times greater than the fastest bullet fired by man on earth. At these velocities a small particle even the size of a pinhead can penetrate a great deal of shielding and produce tremendous damage to equipment and, of course, to the human body. For this reason much consideration has been given to space exploration tools which would tell us how frequently micrometeorites are encountered and what their energies are.

We are also concerned about meteorites, bigger than micrometeorites, for if one of these even the size of a golf ball struck any modern spacecraft it would completely disintegrate it, and we would have no way of measuring or perhaps even becoming aware of the accident.

With the micrometeorites, however, we can deal scientifically. Most spacecraft carry a flat metallic sheet or a box of carefully measured size and so constructed that each time a micrometeorite or a bit of cosmic dust strikes the surface, the impact produces an electric signal which is transmitted back to earth.

On the Mariner mission to Venus, for example, we found that micrometeorites are much less numerous (by a factor of 1,000 to 1) in space beyond the earth than they are near its surface. The same measure of micrometeorite collisions showed that these particles were even much less prevalent near Venus than they were near earth. This seems to indicate that the magnetic field of earth (and Venus has almost no magnetic field) perhaps traps these small particles traveling through space in somewhat the same way that it traps charged particles in the Van Allen belts. Once trapped in our magnetic field, the micrometeorites may orbit the earth in a more or less circular or even highly elliptical orbit until they lose enough of their speed (energy of motion) to be drawn into our atmosphere and there burned up by friction as shooting stars.

We know, however, that there are other planets in the solar system

8. Spacemen

It is impossible to tell about *all* the men engaged in space activities, for their name is legion. It is hoped that the biographical sketches of a few typical spacemen who have made significant contributions to the great effort will give an idea of what human contributions are required for a successful space program—for that matter, for a successful program in any endeavor, great or small.

The First

Many important scientific and technical discoveries have been made almost simultaneously by two or more people in different parts of the world, apparently working independently. This seems to indicate that, at a certain point in the development of civilization, all the ingredients for the discovery are present: the circumstances, the development of man's understanding of his world to a certain point, the tools or techniques for observing or measuring what is going on in nature, the need for the discovery, and of course the natural phenomena themselves, which may or may not have existed since time immemorial.

This seems to have been the way it was in the discovery of the principle of the reaction motor, which apparently took place in China and Arabia and perhaps in other communities considerably before the dawn of carefully recorded history. Of course, there were caravan routes between China and the Arab worlds, so let us assume that it was a Chinese member of the fireworks guild who discovered the reaction motor. Let us call him Wang Ho.

Wang Ho was a respected member of the fireworks guild. He made firecrackers, and their loud noise, when fired on special holy days, scared away the evil spirits. The fireworks guild also made flares of various colors and furious and evil-smelling smokes, not only to frighten away the demons but also to amuse the people who gathered for the ceremonies. The fireworks guild was a very closely organized affair, much tighter than a modern American union. The knowledge and skills of each guild member were passed down by inheritance to his eldest son who, upon becoming of age—about thirteen or fourteen years after his birth—was initiated into the secrets of the guild with great and horrifying ceremonies.

In spite of his exalted position in relation to the peasants of the land, Wang Ho was dissatisfied with his lot. As he sat on the ground leaning against the mud wall of the guild's compound on a cold winter morning, he cupped a bowl of hot tea in his numbed fingers. As the bowl warmed his hands, he inhaled slowly the fragrant warm steam rising from the bowl and thought bitter thoughts.

His bitterness, as it had among his people for centuries before and would for centuries after Wang Ho, centered about the activities of the war lords. The peasants tilled the land owned by the war lords and lived upon the share of the produce which they were allowed to keep, sometimes selling a pretty daughter into the houses of pleasure in a nearby Chinese city. The guildsmen, such as Wang Ho, considered themselves several steps above the mud-coated and manure-smelling peasants because the guildsman had a trade, the guildsman knew the secrets of making things which no one else knew—secrets which had been handed down to him from his father and his father's father.

But over them all stood the war lord. The war lord tilled no fields, the war lord knew no skill but the sword, no secret but death. The war lord's technique was simple—he gathered about him a group of strong and active peasants who considered anything preferable to tilling the land, and equipped them with weapons, forming a small band of followers. At first he attacked bands only smaller than his or, if he had some imagination, managed by stealth and tactics to destroy bands slightly larger than his own. As soon as the destruction was accomplished he took over the territory the defeated band had previously controlled, sometimes keeping certain surviving members of the defeated band as mercenaries in his own growing army. By this process, the war lord took over as much territory as he could until he ran into a war lord stronger or wilier than himself, or until he ran out of ambition or sometimes, because of China's famines, he just ran out of food and his soldiers became too weak to fight, allowing some war lord from a location less affected by drought or flood to move in on his territory.

These were the thoughts that Wang Ho was thinking as he warmed himself with his morning bowl of tea. The thing that galled him was the fact that the war lords, who knew nothing but struggle and death, treated Wang Ho and all his kind with such contempt, enforcing their imagined superiority with the sword.

Having finished his tea, Wang Ho went slowly into one of the mud-walled buildings around the compound to begin his daily work of making firecrackers. Firecrackers were made by rolling a small tube of dampened paper coated with a sticky clay, setting the tube out to dry in the sun and, once it was dry, filling it with fire powder, inserting a fuse, and crimping the ends. As Wang Ho worked, his small son came into the workroom to watch his father at his trade. Sometimes the crimping in of the ends of the firecrackers did not proceed according to plan, and a firecraker had to be discarded— today it would be known as a "fizzer," one which sputtered and scooted along the ground but did not explode.

As Wang Ho's small son clamored, he gave the child two or three of these. The child took them out into the center of the compound, where a small fire was burning. Wang Ho, tired of his labors and wanting to stretch his back a bit, stepped to the doorway to watch his son's play. The little boy took a burning twig out of the fire and lighted the fuse of one of these imperfect firecrackers. As the fuse burned down, the firecracker zipped across the compound with a phtt that brought it up with a small thump against the mud walls of one of the buildings.

At this moment Wang Ho discovered the reaction engine. The thought crossed his mind, "If I could make such a 'rocket' of a bigger size and attached to an arrow I could become the most fearsome war lord of all and conquer all our enemies and those who oppress us."

Wang Ho was a phlegmatic and not easily excited man; in addition, he had his day's work to finish. But Wang Ho thought about this as he worked, and that night as he and his wife lay down together on their hard bed he told her of his idea.

Womanlike, she was horrified that Wang Ho might consider doing anything which would bring him into conflict with the war lords. But the more Wang Ho thought about it the more the desire for power filled him and the more attractive the idea seemed. The next day he set to work at once to make a rocket big enough to carry an arrow.

Over the next several days he made several of these fire arrows, first trying them out within the compound where they struck harmlessly against a blank mud wall. But as the idea grew in him, so did his contempt for the war lords, and he began to dream of bigger and bigger fire arrows. Shortly he was making them too big to be tested in the compound. He made a half dozen which he decided on the next holy day he would take into the field behind the compound where he could test their capability more fully.

The holy day came at last, and while most of the populace was attending the celebration marked by explosions of firecrackers and burning of flares which Wang Ho and his guild had prepared, Wang Ho himself left the crowd, went to the field behind the compound, and set off one of his fire arrows.

He had pointed it halfway between the sun and the horizon and was amazed and delighted to see that it rose furiously into the air and traveled with a great speed and hissing to bury its point in the earth far from where he stood. As he marveled at its success, he became aware that a party of horsemen had stopped behind him. Turning, he beheld the local war lord, who was as fascinated by the fire arrow's performance as Wang Ho had been. Wang Ho felt his knees begin to tremble and made the proper bow before the war lord, who fixed him with a piercing eye.

As Wang Ho rose from his obeisance, the war lord, whose usual conversational tone was a bellow, shouted, "Wang Ho, what is this fire arrow which flies with such speed and violence over great distances?"

Wang Ho bowed low, despair bowing his heart even lower at being found out so early in his project, and said, "Oh Lord, it is but a plaything."

The war lord said, "I would see more!"

As the war lord's entourage gathered threateningly around Wang Ho, he set up another fire arrow and touched it off. It performed as the first had, whizzing high into the air at great speed and driving deeply into the earth far from where they stood.

The war lord was so pleased that he clapped his hands, his sword rattling in its sheath, and his followers gave cries of delight. The shaggy wild ponies they were riding shook their heads and stamped their feet.

Despair spreading within him, Wang Ho turned toward the war lord and bowed low again.

The war lord said, "I will have these fire arrows for my army. Wang Ho, you are the greatest of the fireworks maker's guild. I shall give you quarters in my palace, many valuables, and beautiful women to amuse you. You will make fire arrows to defeat my enemies. But you must not give the secret to anyone else. Men, seize Wang Ho and bring him with us."

Thus, Wang Ho was the first spaceman. Many hundred years ago he discovered the reaction motor without even the faintest dream that it would one day lift a spaceship of several thousand tons to another planet or to a nearby star.

The Genius

Once in perhaps every half millennium a man comes upon the world stage who seems by nature to be a master of ceremonies: he introduces all the other significant figures in the world scene, giving them lines to say and reasons for being. In the fifteenth century such a man was Leonardo da Vinci. He stood as master of the Italian Renaissance—in everything that was significant about that sudden flowering of civilization in art, science, and engineering Leonardo himself was an expert.

In the twentieth century another man of towering stature stands in the same relationship to the space age—Dr. Theodore von Karman.

Born in Budapest on May 11, 1881, as the son of one of the greatest teachers in Hungary, Dr. Maurice von Karman, from his early youth Theodore was exposed to the stimulating intellectual atmosphere of his parents' home.

He graduated with the highest honors from the Royal Technical University of Budapest in 1902 as a mechanical engineer. Following a period as a research engineer for the Ganz Company, a machinery manufacturer, the young von Karman returned to the study of mathematics, physics, and mechanics at the University of Gottingen in 1906 and received his Ph.D. in 1908. He remained at that university as an assistant professor until 1912.

For the next eighteen years he labored vitally and joyously in the founding and development of the Aeronautical Institute in the University of Aachen, with time out for a tour of duty in the Austro-Hungarian Aviation Corps during the First World War.

Von Karman's brilliance as its director attracted students to the institute from all over the world, and Aachen became a leading aeronautical center. Von Karman's father died when Theodore was only thirty-four; a few years later his mother and his brilliant sister, Dr. Josephine A. Karman, made their home with Theodore. As in his early days, von Karman again found himself in a stimulating intellectual atmosphere; these people seemed to act and react upon each other in a way which might be likened to the action of a cyclotron upon a charged particle, increasing the energy and brilliance of each. This association is believed to have been a significant influence in von Karman's success as a most remarkable teacher and engineer and as an inspiration to his students and associates.

Von Karman first came to the United States in 1926 at the invitation of the Daniel Guggenheim Fund for the Promotion of Aeronautics. From that point on, his time and energy seemed about equally divided between the Institute of Aachen and the Guggenheim Foundation in Pasadena, California. In 1930 he became director of the Guggenheim Laboratory at the California Institute of Technology and took up permanent residence in the United States. As at the institute at Aachen, so with the institute at Pasadena, he was a magnet for brilliant and inquiring intellects from every part of the world. One of the chief elements of his genius was his ability to combine theory and experiment in a novel approach to the teaching of engineering which resulted in the development of a new kind of aeronautical engineer, destined to play an important role in twentieth century space exploration.

In 1944 von Karman organized a scientific group to advise the U.S. Air Force in the fields of jet propulsion, supersonic aerodynamics, electronics, and other technologies which might be applied to the solution of military problems.

In 1941 von Karman had taken a group of interested students into a dry mountain canyon, called the Arroyo Seco, in the San Gabriel Mountains above Pasadena to conduct experiments in propulsion and rocket firing. Out of this simple example of von Karman's ability to combine theory with experiment grew the JATO bottles which provided jet-assisted takeoff for World War II aircraft; there also developed the Aerojet General Corporation whose business at first was to make these JATO bottles; and, further, there evolved the JPL which produced early military rockets for the U.S. Army during the following decade.

One of the fascinating things about von Karman's scientific interests is that his major lines of inquiry and the principles he discovered seem equally applicable to the improvement of aircraft and the development of spacecraft. Much of his work in these years was in the fields of fluid mechanics and heat transfer. As aircraft flew faster and faster the flow of air over air foils, and the resulting turbulence and heating effects became increasingly important to aircraft design. The

Site of early rocket experiments by von Karman and students at California Institute of Technology. (*Jet Propulsion Laboratory*)

science which could solve these problems meant vastly improved aircraft, which eventually broke the sound barrier and evolved into a series of rocket ships such as the X-15, which is perhaps more like a winged spacecraft than a true airplane.

These same studies on high velocity flow of air, and ionized and superheated gases became of basic importance to the design of efficient rocket engines, in which the gases flow at rates of several thousand, rather than several hundred, miles per hour; instead of flowing over an air foil they thunder through a rocket nozzle to provide thrust to lift a spacecraft into orbit.

In addition to being an intellectual genius, von Karman was a genius at the human level. Rarely found in a single individual was his combination of great intellectual power and real love for and enjoyment of his fellow man which was expressed in an interest in the activities of each individual with whom he associated. This made him a brilliant and effective teacher who inspired his students and so infused them with his own knowledge and his own approach to the seeking of knowledge that there is hardly an aerospace industry of any importance in the world which does not claim an important functionary owing allegiance to von Karman. In an even broader sense, this same humanity of von Karman's contributed greatly to good will and good professional relationships among scientists and engineers of many countries of the world.

Von Karman loved beautiful women (although he never married), strong cigars, and a liquor called Slivovitz. He had a gentle humor best exemplified by his favorite definition of a Hungarian—his own nationality—as "a man who goes into a revolving door behind you and comes out ahead."

His contributions have affected the design and production of all modern aircraft and missiles, yet his greatest contribution is that he was able to plant his intellectual seed in the minds of others who would cultivate, nurture, and bring it to a harvest which even he could not have imagined in the eighty-one years before his death in May of 1963.

The Provocateur

In the great gold rush of scientific research—men probing the earth and the cosmos for nuggets of information—there are certain men

Dr. Theodore von Karman, dapper as usual, working out some calculations on the wing of a plane being used in early JATO developments for the Army, (*Jet Propulsion Laboratory*)

around whom exciting things seem to happen. It is often difficult to tell if these men are truly the discoverers, because the things that happen around them are usually team efforts—although the members of the team may be scattered about the face of the earth, their only contact being the exchange of information. Sometimes, of course, the team is a closely knit group from a laboratory, a university, or some technical society. In the presence of these peculiar men who, for lack of a better word, we can call provocateurs of science, ideas seem to sprout from the ground and materialize in space, growing rapidly to some useful maturity and flowering in great cooperative efforts or in what the scientists and engineers call hardware: machines, devices, or electronic circuits that embody new ideas and accomplish things never accomplished before.

Sometimes these unusual men, who seem to act as catalysts in the process of the development of human thought, turn out to be scientific administrators capable of organizing and managing huge scientific and engineering efforts involving hundreds or thousands of men and millions or billions of dollars. But the talent of the administrator is not their hallmark because many of them never seem to administer anything but their own time; nevertheless, when they are present, ideas take shape, new discoveries are made, new techniques devised, and things happen!

A man who seems to embody both of these talents—administration and the simple yet marvelous development of scientific concepts in groups—is James A. Van Allen, head of the department of physics at the University of Iowa, in Iowa City.

After a corn-belt youth spent in the beautiful little midwestern village of Mt. Pleasant, Iowa, as the son of the town's leading attorney and civic figure, Van Allen went to Iowa Wesleyan College in Mt. Pleasant, where he is chiefly remembered by his professor of physics, Thomas Poulter, not as a scientist but as a person. Jim Van Allen was quiet, unassuming, and exhibited a maturity which made his professors regard him more as a professional associate rather than a student.

With his father's encouragement Jim had begun before the age of twelve to spend his spare time on technical pursuits, building a machine capable of high-voltage discharges, and other devices of a mechanical and electronic nature.

Jim's father had inculcated in him the strong middle-western virtues of regard for education, worthwhile reading, and the habit of using his time to the fullest possible degree. But perhaps the real secret is that Jim was born with or early acquired a tremendous drive for accomplishment of whatever goal attracted him.

Van Allen's college days at Iowa Wesleyan brought him into early contact with high-level scientific endeavor, for Poulter was chief scientist for the second Byrd Antarctic Expedition of 1933–1935. The physics department at Iowa Wesleyan was the scene of the development, assembly, and test of much of the scientific equipment used on this expedition. Undergraduate Jim Van Allen took an active and enthusiastic part in this work. Some of the equipment with which Van Allen came in contact at this time was intended for the measurement of cosmic rays near the South Pole. Cosmic rays are best measured at the poles and at high altitudes above the earth's surface—this early contagion infected Van Allen with an interest in the upper atmosphere and in the space beyond it.

At the end of World War II, a Colonel Toftoy (later a major general in the U.S. Army) was largely responsible for what was known as "Operation Paper Clip." This was a then highly secret activity directed at bringing more than a hundred of Germany's top rocket experts to the United States. The effort began before V-E Day and continued afterward until the United States and Russia, between them, had largely divided up the intellectual spoils of the victory over Germany. Toftoy also ordered the capture and shipment to White Sands Proving Ground in the United States of more than one hundred V-2 rockets. Some of these were completely assembled vehicles but most of them comprised components which were assembled and tested in this country. Toftoy was a man of vision, appreciating the importance of scientific as well as military activities. With this in mind he arranged that every captured V-2 sent aloft should carry as a part of its payload scientific instrumentation suitable for exploring the upper atmosphere. He asked Dr. Merle A. Truve, director of the Applied Physics Laboratory at Johns Hopkins University, to assign some outstanding young scientist to guide this program on upper atmosphere research. Truve sent Van Allen to White Sands.

The results of the V-2 upper atmosphere research were so interesting that an upper-atmosphere rocket research panel, with Van Allen as chairman from 1947 to 1958, was formed. The group soon ran out of V-2s, so Van Allen negotiated with Aerojet General Corporation (then Aerojet Engineering Corporation) the development and construction of a "sounding" rocket called the Aerobee—a much more economical device than the V-2. The Aerobee program was initiated with a first launch on November 23, 1947, and continued through more than 170 firings over a ten-year period to measure solar radiation, sky brightness, composition of the upper atmosphere, and, of course, cosmic and other radiations in near space, up to sixty miles above the earth's surface.

As an example of the special catalytic influence of such men as Van Allen, a dinner party discussion in his home on an April evening in 1950 with Dr. Sydney Chapman, perhaps the world's foremost geophysicist, and others, resulted in the idea for an international geophysical year.

Through the efforts of the dinner party guests, who were all technical people with the exception of Mr. Lloyd Birkner, active in the State Department in the organization and direction of military assistance programs for the North Atlantic Pact countries, the idea spread rapidly through the world scientific community. Mr. Birkner presented the plan at the Mixed Commissions on the Ionosphere in Brussels, Belgium, in July of 1950 and the time for the eighteen-month geophysical year was established as July 1, 1957, through December 31, 1958. This period was chosen because there would be a time of great sunspot activity and several eclipses. Incidentally, the date would be the twenty-fifth anniversary of the second Polar Year—a similar effort in international scientific cooperation. In planning for the I.G.Y. there was much discussion about launching an earth satellite, an idea which far-sighted United States scientists

High altitude photograph of earth's surface, similar to those made with early sounding rockets. (NASA *photo*)

had long advocated and for which Van Allen had actively campaigned in 1948 in a paper he read at the International Union of Geodesy and Geophysics in Oslo, Norway.

Nevertheless it was seven years later, in 1955, before government approval of a United States earth satellite program under the I.G.Y. was gained. As chairman of the responsible committee, Van Allen was overjoyed and immediately called a symposium of the Rocket and Satellite Research Committee for January 1956.

The first I.G.Y. conference on satellites was held in Barcelona in August of 1956 to gain international cooperation for the effort and to give other participating countries an opportunity to submit their proposals for instruments to be carried on the first earth satellite. Dr. I. P. Bardin and others represented the Soviet Union in working out instrumentation arrangements and establishment of standard radio frequencies on which the satellite would broadcast, so that its transmissions could be picked up at tracking stations throughout the world.

It was the consensus of Van Allen and others that the Jupiter-C rocket, then under development at the Army Ballistic Missile Research Center at Huntsville, Alabama, under Dr. Wernher von Braun was the ideal vehicle with which to launch the first earth satellite and the only one known to be in a condition ready for such an undertaking. For some still obscure reason, however, the government decided that the Vanguard rocket, then under development by the Navy, should orbit the first satellite. This was a great blow to Van Allen and his organization because they did not believe that the Vanguard could be readied in time. A careful study of the situation by important scientists in the program resulted in a barrage of telegrams which went unheeded in Washington. Van Allen and his group had already started to develop the instrumentation for the Jupiter-C vehicle; Washington's refusal to use this rocket meant that the instrumentation had to be scaled down and redesigned to meet the smaller weight and dimension requirements of the Vanguard rocket. In fact, some experiments had to be left out altogether.

The Russians, surely highly amused by this bungling of American bureaucracy, apparently decided somewhere in this period to launch their own satellite, using intercontinental ballistic missiles we did not realize they had fully developed. Thus, on October 4, 1957, without regard to the rest of the world scientific community, the Russians launched Sputnik I. The United States was still trying to get the Vanguard vehicle in shape to launch a "grapefruit-size" earth satellite.

Despair is a luxury which people engaged in the arduous pursuit of scientific information, where there are perhaps a hundred failures or more for each success, cannot afford. At the time of the Sputnik launching, Van Allen was far off in the South Pacific on the U.S.S. *Glacier* as part of his activities in connection with the Geophysical Year. Dr. Pickering of the JPL, upon hearing of the Sputnik launching decided that it was time to take some action, protocol or no protocol. In conjunction with von Braun of the Army Ballistic Missile Agency (ABMA) he had earlier devised a plan to launch an American satellite using the frowned-upon Jupiter-C missile. Attempts to get Van Allen's approval for this plan through the communication systems of the Navy and the Coast Guard failed. As a last resort, Pickering simply sent a message to Van Allen via Western Union asking if he would approve the transfer of the earth satellite experiment to JPL and ABMA. Only two days later, to the jubilant amazement of all, a cable was received from Van Allen okaying the shift.

Many military men, startled by the Russian success, were now eager to have an American satellite launched, regardless of which service furnished the vehicle and got the credit!

In the eighty-three days between November 9, 1957 and January 31, 1958, the JPL–ABMA team adapted the scientific payload to the Jupiter-C missile. This process was greatly simplified by the foresightedness of Van Allen, who had designed the payload for use with either missile. Getting all systems checked, the launching vehicle on the pad at Cape Kennedy, and the countdown completed was a tremendous task for eighty days. On January 31, 1958, Explorer I was successfully launched!

Although the original participants in the I.G.Y. had agreed on the satellite plan put forward by the United States for sharing information to be gained from the satellite, the Russians—having made it first into space—were very reluctant and extremely slow about sharing the information received from Sputnik I. This attitude cast unfortunate doubt upon the nature of the information they may have gained from their Sputnik I. Their practice was to release no information until the United States had released information from Explorer I; then the Russians would come in with a "Me, too—only I was first," kind of report.

There is no doubt, however, about the fact that the United States satellite, Explorer I, reported much new information on near space to the world scientific community. Its discovery of the Van Allen radiation belts is the most important piece of knowledge to come out of the I.G.Y.

Thus it was that one of those unique scientists who seem to have a knack for "making things happen" was responsible for the world-wide adoption of the satellite concept, and for the launching of the first United States satellite—he was probably responsible for the launching of the Russian Sputnik as well!

The Gambler

There is something almost reminiscent of the peak of the Aztec civilization about the launching pads at Cape Kennedy. Instead of the steep-sided, sun-aspiring, stone pyramid fitted together with such consummate skill—and no mortar—that a knife blade cannot be inserted between the stone blocks, there is the intricately and marvelously made missile, surrounded by a complex steel structure called a gantry.

The missile, of course, not only aspires to the sun, it can actually reach the sun, if its launchers so intend—the high priests of the Aztecs, atop their pyramid, only yearned for it.

The sacred fire at the apex of the stone pyramid is replaced by the "smoke-like" vapor from the LOX, as the liquid oxygen boils off from the missile's propellant tanks. No sacrificial fire was ever prepared with more care, nor half as much skill in avoiding contamination, as is the liquid oxygen that goes into an Atlas missile.

Instead of the long ceremonial march up the steep-sided stone pyramid, flight after stone flight of high steps, by the feather-plumed priests and their sacrificial charge, the astronaut and his handlers are whisked silently to the entry platform in a swift electric elevator, which carries the helmeted astronaut and his helpers to the top of the gantry, and a little walkway that leads them to the entrance of the space capsule in which he hopes to orbit the earth.

No matter what the symbolism or the dress, if you want to make a spiritual contact with the gods of the sun or a human orbit of this beautiful planet earth, some one human being must face the ultimate moment of truth, willing to lay down his life if necessary for the things in which he believes. This is the astronaut!

In twentieth-century terms, if you want a piloted flight of a spacecraft in orbit around the earth, to the moon, or to one of the planets,

John Glenn atop the Mercury Atlas at liftoff. (NASA *photo*)

some man must be willing to strap himself into the launching couch in more or less cramped quarters and try it. He must ride the flame into the heavens and, if he is to return to earth again, he must pass through the flames of atmospheric re-entry upon his return. Somebody has to do it first!

No matter how much training, no matter how much physical, intellectual, and emotional preparation, the man has to face the moment of truth in which it is determined whether generations, even hundreds of years of scientific questioning and human speculation and development of precise theories and concepts have been reasonably accurate.

At the same time it is a test of the millions of engineering manhours spent in converting these theories and concepts into flyable hardware, the vehicle in which the astronaut rides, the booster missile which will lift him into orbit, the carefully planned re-entry devices which keep him from burning to a cinder when he returns to the earth's atmosphere. It is equally a validation of the skill, workmanship, dedication, and absolute accuracy of thirty or forty thousand people who have actually worked upon the myriad parts which go to make up the amazing device which is a spacecraft and the boosters necessary to put it into orbit. In the first twenty seconds after the countdown to $T = 0$ and the command "Fire!" the verity of all this planning and effort is almost instantaneously established or denied.

Colonel John H. Glenn is an ideal example of the kind of men who have piloted and will pilot our spacecraft, whether in orbit about the earth or in trips to the moon, Venus, Mars, and beyond. There are some who say that it is necessary to pick an individual of phlegmatic temperament and little imagination for this kind of assignment. They reckon without the complexity of the task. They do not look at the picture of Glenn embracing Scott Carpenter after the second manned orbital space flight for the United States. This photograph was charged with an emotion impossible for an unimaginative man.

Ritual is a great sustainer of man in times of stress. The ritual of the Aztecs as they mounted the steps of the stone pyramid toward the sacrificial altar and the sacred fire was child's play compared to the elaborate and disciplined ritual necessary for the launching of a spacecraft—functionally necessary to insure performance of the highly complex man-machine system and incidentally useful in sustaining the individual who must execute the complicated routines required of a spacecraft pilot.

In the pilot's flight report in the NASA publication, "Results of the First United States Manned Orbital Space Flight," February 20, 1962, John Glenn says:

> While the spacecraft hatch was being secured, a bolt was broken and had to be repaired. During this time I was busy going over my check list and monitoring the spacecraft instruments.
>
> Many people were concerned about my mental state during this and earlier delays. . . . Humans always have fear of an unknown situation—this is normal. The important thing is what we do about it. . . . The best antidote to fear is to know all we can about a situation. . . . During the years of preparation for Project Mercury the unknown areas have been shrunk, we feel, to an acceptable level.

Through the work necessary to "shrink the unknown areas," through the practicing of specific routines required to successfuly launch and pilot a spacecraft, through the highest kind of courage and dedication to an ideal, John Glenn, coming from an undistinguished midwestern background up through the disciplined training of our military institutions and broadened by years of experience as a test pilot of aircraft, made possible the first United States manned orbital space flight.

The Symbol

Most peoples of the earth need a symbol and a rallying point for their major efforts and contests. Americans are no different from others in this respect, and although Robert Goddard, perhaps the first modern man to recognize the importance and usefulness of rockets, was an American, we chose for our symbol of the space age an import, a German named Wernher von Braun.

At the end of World War II when both the free world and the Russians were scrambling for whatever brains they could find in Europe, Wernher von Braun was a real prize and a status symbol in the beginning of the cold war with Russia. He was brought to the United States in September 1945 shortly after Goddard's death on August 10 of that year. He was of noble German birth, had been director of Germany's V-2 project which rained such haphazard devastation upon London, and he was a handsome and gregarious person. He had a tremendous affinity for cameras, and newspapers and other media were soon filled with pictures of him staring vigorously into space and displaying his prognathous jaw.

Despite the demands of his unofficial position as a symbol of America's emerging interest in rocketry, much credit is due to Wernher von Braun for the development of the missile which placed America's first satellite in orbit.

What manner of man is this?

Von Braun, in short, is the quintessence of the space age. He has been inspired and influenced by and has absorbed something of almost every major personality, organization, or concept in the current space effort throughout the world. He is the quintessence of the space age in much the same way that a diamond is the ultimate form of carbon. Von Braun, like the diamond, glitters and has value more for the fact that he *is* than for the fact that he *does*. This does not mean that von Braun has not been responsible for some important work, both in Germany and this country, but he differs from some of the space pioneers in that he does not have a driving compulsion for research and development like Goddard, for example, who carried on his pioneering efforts in the face of insurmountable odds and with little recognition.

Von Braun is of a different era. He symbolizes the space age to many people and has been able to enjoy, interspersed with some rather desperate times in Germany, the plaudits of the multitude and the kudos of a hero. For many people he has been and is "Mr. Space."

The man who came along at the uniquely right time in history to achieve all these things, born in 1912 to the Baron and Baroness Magnus Freiherr von Braun on an ancestral family estate in Silesia, Wernher von Braun early responded to the cultured environment into which he had been born by taking a serious interest in music and the study of languages. At first he showed very poor results in mathematics; it turned out, however, that what he needed was a more challenging presentation of the material, and at a subsequent school he emerged with such outstanding performance in mathematics that he was made an assistant to the instructor in teaching advanced classes.

Von Braun's mother, the baroness, was a very exceptional person and an amateur astronomer. Early in her son's life she gave him a telescope, and through the hobby of astronomy he happened upon an article in a magazine describing an imaginary trip to the moon. This seemed to set him upon the course that the rest of his life took. As he said later, he felt that interplanetary travel was a task worth dedicating his life to—"Not just to stare at the moon and planets through a telescope, but to travel through the celestial regions and actually explore the mysteries of the universe." At this point he believed he knew the feeling Columbus must have had.

During von Braun's youth a great many important scientists in Germany were actively experimenting in rocket research. Such names as Max Valier, Freidrich W. Sander, Fritz von Opel, and Hermann Oberth, the author of the book, *The Rocket into Interplanetary Space*. In addition, Germany's central position in Europe meant that many of the people interested in rocketry and space travel journeyed back and forth through Germany or met there under the aegis of a rocket society which had been formed by German scientists and engineers in 1927 for the study of rockets and space travel.

One of the people who most influenced young Wernher von Braun was Willy Ley, who is so well known for his books, produced with Chesley Bonestell, on space and space travel. Ley took a liking to young von Braun, used him to stage what was perhaps the first display of space travel in a Berlin department store in the early 1930's and subsequently brought him into close contact with Hermann Oberth.

About this time the young German Rocket Society managed to acquire an old ammunition dump outside Berlin, which was promptly named "Rocket Field, Berlin." Although there was not much rocket firing at this location in the early days, there was much good talk. The place served as a launching pad for ideas if not rockets, and there was always shelter and food for those who were having a hard time making ends meet while they investigated the matters which would vitally affect the future of the human race.

Von Braun and some of his cohorts at "Rocket Field, Berlin," were interviewed in 1932 by representatives of the German Army Ordinance Department, with the result that von Braun became a civilian employee of the German Army in November of that year. He was sent to study at the University of Berlin under physics professor Erich Schumann, who was also responsible for the research programs of the German Army Ordinance Department. In this manner, the German Army Ordinance Department facilities at Kummersdorf were placed at von Braun's disposal for experimental work required to complete his thesis. He received his doctorate in 1934.

During this time, von Braun, like other German nobility and men of substance, believed that Hitler was a funny fanatic with a Charlie Chaplin-type mustache.

In January of 1933, of course, Hitler came to power. Scanning the Versailles Treaty, the German high command discovered that there was no reference to rockets in the prohibition against rearming which the Allies had placed upon Germany. Consequently, the V-2 rocket was conceived early in the thirties; it was to be a heavy and powerful weapon which was to have at least a 160-mile range. Thus, von Braun was almost at once shifted from working on tiny experimental rockets to a project involving the production of a 12-ton missile specified to be capable of 3,350-mile-per-hour velocity, carrying a one-ton warhead. The magnitude of the concept was amazing for those years.

The V-2 program which started in 1936 and exploded on British soil in late 1944 was under the command of a man named Dornberger, but much credit is due von Braun, who was able to "soak up" knowledge from all fields of scientific endeavor and apply it to the V-2 rocket program in which he was engaged.

In 1945, when the Red Army was rapidly approaching the V-2 center at Peenemünde, von Braun received conflicting orders: one set from the Army, commanding his group to help in the battle against the advancing Red troops, and a second set of orders from the high command in Germany, instructing the group to move west. Having the opportunity to choose, von Braun decided to surrender to the Americans because he knew America's reputation for individual freedom and human rights, and he felt that the built-in system of checks and balances of the American government would assure that the information he was able to turn over to them would not be used wantonly.

Von Braun called his group together and asked them to make individual decisions as to which one of the sets of conflicting orders they would follow. All but one decided to join the Allied forces.

There followed a cloak-and-dagger period in which the game was to try to stay alive and reach a point at which they could successfully surrender to the Americans. Their problem was complicated by the fact that although the high command indicated that von Braun's group could surrender to the West, the secret police had been given orders to destroy the members of von Braun's team rather than let them reach the Allied lines.

Von Braun had already had experience with Himmler's group in an internal Nazi political struggle in which Himmler had tried to get his hands on the V-2 program in defiance of army ordinance. In this struggle Himmler had had von Braun arrested and brought to trial on trumped-up charges in an attempt to remove him from the scene. It was only intervention with Hitler personally by Dornberger, explaining that there would be no V-2 production unless von Braun were released, that saved his life in this case.

With this background, von Braun did not want to get involved further with the SS, and finally worked out an arrangement by which his group could be distributed among villages in the Bavarian Alps, where he was quartered in a ski lodge.

After the Allied victory, von Braun, learning of it in his mountain retreat, set out to find some way to surrender to the Americans.

The plan finally evolved had von Braun's brother, Magnus, who spoke English well, bicycle down the mountainside until he encountered an American patrol. An American private, from Sheboygan, Wisconsin, brought von Braun to the Counter-Intelligence Corps Headquarters of his unit, where von Braun, unappreciated by the American official, was told to return the next day with his colleagues.

As interviews with the German scientists were undertaken by the Counter-Intelligence Corps, field reports began to flow into headquarters, and (then Colonel) H. N. Toftoy, at that time stationed in Paris, learned of the windfall of scientific brain power which had been discovered in the Bavarian Alps.

Toftoy finally had to go to Washington to get enough support from the American government (Departments of War, State, and Commerce) to bring an agreed 100 scientists to the United States. Toftoy and von Braun, between them, selected out of the approximately 450 of von Braun's group, 127 of Germany's finest scientists to be invited to the United States.

When von Braun and his cohorts came to the United States, of course, they came as enemy aliens. Von Braun himself had to be escorted by James P. Hamill, a U.S. Army major, on a 24-hour-a-day basis on his trip across the country to Ft. Bliss near El Paso, Texas. There it had been planned to establish this group of "Paper Clip" scientists in support of the United States rocket program.

Finally, through some kind of high-level hankypanky, von Braun and others were taken to Juarez, Mexico, where they could enter this country from our friendly neighbor to the south and thus be approved for citizenship in the United States.

Von Braun's first assignment after reaching this country and settling in Ft. Bliss was to instruct American crews in the difficult and intricate tasks of assembling and firing V-2 rockets. A quantity of these had been discovered near Peenemünde shortly after V-E Day.

The testing of these assembled German V-2s was to take place at White Sands Proving Ground, New Mexico, which was near the town of Roswell, New Mexico, where America's Goddard had first demonstrated the possibilities of the rocket. Some early high-altitude experiments (a few of them mentioned in the discussion of Van Allen's activities) were conducted with these early V-2s and the WAC Corporal rockets which formed their second stage.

When the war closed, however, appropriations and effort were cut back in typical American fashion in what then was generally regarded as a purely military project. Von Braun, who had his early rocket efforts well supported by the German military machine, was not accustomed to getting along on such "short rations." He applied his usual scientific perception to the problem. Von Braun decided that what was needed was to sell space to the American public so that through the medium of the ballot box they would make their desires known to their elected officials, and increase appropriations to a level sufficient to permit aggressive prosecution of his programs.

With this in mind he set out on a campaign which would have done credit to the world's top door-to-door salesman: speaking at scientific and technical meetings, publishing articles in popular and technical magazines, and appearing before any group which would hear him—and these were a great number!

Von Braun's sales campaign started in 1949, and in 1951 the shock of Korea sent American military appropriations zooming; von Braun and his group were moved to Huntsville, Alabama, where was located the Army's Redstone Arsenal, subsequently renamed the George C. Marshall Space Flight Center at the time it was turned over to NASA in December of 1959.

At Huntsville, von Braun and his crew went furiously to work in an effort which resulted in the Redstone and the Jupiter Intermediate Range Ballistic Missiles (IRBM). Huntsville, which had once been known as the "Watercress Capital of the World," now became "Rocket City, U.S.A."

After Sputnik, and when the Navy's Vanguard rocket failed, it was von Braun's Jupiter-C missile that lifted America's first satellite into space in January of 1957. It was he and General Medaris, then commander of the Huntsville activity, who cooperated with JPL's Dr. Pickering in using Van Allen's instruments to orbit America's first satellite just eighty-three days after the go-ahead from Washington.

It may be that von Braun represents the truth of the old concept of "to the manner born." He seems to carry on all of his multifarious technical activities almost as if with his left hand, while he obligingly meets the public, the press, and radio and television audiences. Even this he does with seeming ease and an offhand sense of position befitting a popular hero. He looks more like a movie star or a professional platform lecturer than he does the public's usual conception of a scientist or engineer.

In addition, he seems to have another characteristic sometimes not found in scientific personalities—a deep and abiding faith in the immortality of man and in the existence of a Divine Being Who has so carefully ordered this wonderful universe that Wernher would like us all to explore with his own wonderful rockets. His natural religious interests seem to have flowered in the free and (comparatively) religious atmosphere of America and he now attends church regularly and makes his belief in an all-wise God who orders things in the universe a part of his attitude toward life.

It may be that, through some of the devices Wernher has helped to build, man will gain increasing insight into von Braun's convictions in this area as well as in the field of rocketry and space travel.

The Technician

The technician shall have no name, for his name is legion. Everywhere, technical-establishment research moves forward on such as these. Napoleon said that an army moves on its belly. A more apt analogy might be that a tank moves forward on multiple wheels and tracks and a technician is one of these, taking the grinding load day after day, doing the gut-busting work that is part of every technical advance. When the chips are down, he delivers.

We shall call Joe Smith a technician, not because he is a technician in the usual job-description sense—he may be a Ph.D. or a man with no degree—but simply because he is concerned either with the techniques of the scientific method or with developing a specific scientific technique to accomplish a purpose.

For example, let us assume that Joe Smith is developing radar techniques suitable for exploring nearby planets. For experimental purposes it is not always possible to have a planet of the kind you want at a range in which you are interested, nor is it practical to use extremely expensive, high-powered equipment for experimental work. Consequently, much of the basic experimenting is done on a scaled-down radar range atop some ridge or across some flat desert valley where there is nothing to obstruct the radar "view." At one side of the valley is a plastic dome housing radar equipment of, let us say, 1/1000 the power of the equipment expected actually to be used to investigate the surface of nearby planets. Consequently, the frequency used in this experimental equipment is 1,000 times as great (the wavelength 1,000 times as small) as it would be in the actual equipment.

On the opposite side of this long desert valley is the "target," raised on a ridge so that it will not be lost in the echoes from background "snow or trash," as the technicians call unwanted reflections of radar signals.

The target may actually be a scale model of what the investigators suspect the planet to be investigated looks like. Or it may be some known but irregular geometric shape so that the investigators can determine the effect of different target contours upon the radar "echoes" which come back to the receiver. In addition, patches of material of different radar "reflectivity" may be used to simulate hard rock, forests, or dusty plains, etc.

In the plastic, "radar-transparent" dome in which the equipment is housed, Joe Smith is hard at work at a bench, puzzling over the radar reflection trace which has just been received from the last transmission toward a target across the valley. Beside this trace, on the bench, he has spread out the big blueline print which shows the circuitry used in the radar equipment behind him in the plastic igloo. On another bench a helper is busily soldering some changes into a "plug-in" section of the circuit called a module.

It is approximately one o'clock in the morning and Joe Smith and his helper have been steadily at work since eight o'clock the previous morning. They did get some lunch when the chow truck came by, but no chow truck comes by at supper time and so supper was passed up.

In one corner of the igloo is a desk which is used as the laboratory "office." On the desk a telephone jingles uncertainly. The helper drops his soldering iron and walks unsteadily over to the desk and picks up the phone, listens quietly for a moment and, without responding, turns and says over his shoulder, "It's for you, Joe."

Joe runs his hand distractedly through his hair, turns away from the tracing and the blueline before him, throwing down a pencil as he does so, and walks over to the desk in long strides, snatching up the phone to say, "Joe Smith speaking."

Over the line he hears the voice of Mrs. Joe Smith. It is obvious that she has been crying and is only restraining further sobs with an effort.

Her voice comes quavering over the line. "Joe?" she asks.

Joe's voice fails him through long hours of disuse, and he only croaks into the phone, clears his throat and says harshly, "Yes?"

"Joe, where are you, honey?"

Joe, who has been working not only this day and night but in this same manner for the past five weeks on the same problem with no results, at least none that he can now detect, is in no mood for this kind of game.

"Where the hell do you think I am!" he explodes. "I'm at the lab, of course."

At this point Mrs. Joe breaks into active sobs and can't talk any more.

Joe, contrite, says, "Honey?"

No answer.

"Elaine?" he says.

This only brings on a fresh burst of crying.

"Honey, talk to me," he says. "I'm sorry, but I'm awfully busy and I can't waste this time. What is it you want?"

At this point the receiver at Mrs. Joe's end of the line is slowly dropped into the cradle, turning off further conversation.

Joe looks at the telephone in his hand with a puzzled expression for a moment and then slams it into the cradle and strides back to the table at which he was working. He addresses himself again to the faint tracings of the radar echo and looks from the tracings to the blueline, from time to time making tentative marks on a scratch pad with a pencil. After a few minutes of this, during which he seems obviously agitated and keeps running his hands through his hair he throws the pencil down and stands up, giving a hitch to his trousers and turns to his helper.

"Bob," he says, "I think we've had it for tonight. I don't believe I can stick it any more. Besides, Elaine calling up got me all off the track."

Bob looks up from his soldering, with bloodshot eyes to match Joe's and says, "Maybe you're right. Tomorrow's another day."

Without more ado they get their jackets from a coat hanger in one corner of the room, shrug into them and go out the door, locking it behind them.

In Joe's car they climb briefly out of the valley over a low mountain pass and into a small town beyond the ridge. It isn't quite two o'clock, and the bar is still open. Joe looks at Bob and Bob looks at Joe; without speaking, Joe turns the car into the parking lot. They get out and go in and hunch up on adjacent bar stools. Bob asks for a beer, and Joe orders scotch and soda.

For a few minutes they drink in silence, and then Joe turns to Bob and says, "We've only got another eleven days."

Bob, knowing what's on Joe's mind, says, "I can't figure out what the hell's the matter with this rig. I've been over every connection and every possible source of intercoupling in the whole lashup and I can't find anything to account for the distortion we're getting."

Joe shakes his head and, looking into his drink says, "I know, and I've been over the theory and the mathematics time and time again and I can't find anything wrong there either, but we just aren't getting the kind of return we ought to have."

After a moment or two of silence Bob looks up nervously and says, "What do you suppose the boss will do if we don't make it?"

Joe, who is just finishing his drink, slams the glass down hard on the bar; a look of grimness comes to his face and a glint to his eye as he says to Bob, "We've got to make it!"

The bartender calls out from the end of the bar, "Closing in five minutes, gentlemen. Anybody wants another drink, order it now."

Joe and Bob look at each other briefly and, without shaking their heads or any outward sign, leave the bar and get back in the car.

As Joe starts the engine, he says to Bob, "How about bunking with you tonight in your trailer? If I go home it will be another twenty miles each way, and I'm pooped."

Bob nods and says, "Any time."

Without further word they drive to Bob's trailer and go in. The desert night is cold so Bob lights the butane heater while Joe falls upon the couch and is almost instantly asleep. Bob is only moments behind him in undressing and climbing into his own bed.

At six-thirty the next morning the alarm rings and both men are up, taking quick showers in the trailer and falling back into their clothes to return to Joe's car and stop in the nearby village for a quick breakfast before going back to the plastic igloo where their beloved and cursed equipment is housed.

The things that happened on the eleventh day before the deadline are repeated on the tenth day, the ninth day, the eighth day, and the seventh day, with one exception: Mrs. Joe doesn't call any more and Joe Smith is so tired and so preoccupied and so desperate with his problems that he doesn't call her either.

On the sixth day before the deadline, about two o'clock in the afternoon, Joe suddenly straightens up from the crouch he has been maintaining over the tracing and the blueline of the circuit—he straightens up as though he had been stabbed in the posterior with a sharp instrument. He stares in disbelief at the circuit for a long time, making some hasty calculations on the ever-present scratch pad.

Finally he throws down the pencil and lets out a long breath which ends in "Damn!"

Bob looks up from his everlasting tinkering with the hardware and says, "What gives?"

Joe answers with a long string of unprintable expletives and winds up with "I'll be a monkey's uncle!"

Bob, beginning to catch the feeling of excitement, asks again, "What gives!?"

"Just a little old sign," says Joe. "I had a positive where I should have had a negative and I threw this particular block of the circuitry off."

Bob starts to swear now. "What! Where?" And he rushes over to look while Joe points out on the circuit diagram and illustrates with further mathematical calculations on the scratch pad what he is talking about.

"This gives me an idea," says Bob, and he goes back to his own work, pulling out a module that he had been over at least seventeen times before, and looking at it more critically.

"If that's the case, this is probably where the coupling is. And that's why we're getting this distortion." He looks questioningly at Joe, who nods his head slowly. "Yeah, could be."

With this Bob goes to work furiously on the module, unsoldering two or three connections, replacing this component with that, re-arranging a couple of wires, and soldering the whole back together again. Once it's done he puts it back in the chassis in the place where it belongs, while Joe sits nervously smoking a cigarette.

"I sure *hope* we got it this time!" he breathes fervently.

With great deliberation, both men go about "firing up" the equipment again and making it ready for another test. When the complicated electronic gear has come up to steady-state operating condition, the antenna is trained upon the target across the valley and the signal is transmitted toward the target, to be reflected back and received in the plastic igloo where the two are working. This time the trace comes through beautifully, without distortion. The target is rotated by remote control and the trace appears perfect on the recorder.

Both men look at the perfect trace in stunned bewilderment, unbelieving that after all the struggle they have put into this thing it is finally working. At last Joe shuts off the equipment. They turn to look at each other and without any obvious signal suddenly begin banging each other and whooping for joy and prancing around the room in a sort of Indian war dance.

Finally, breathless, Joe says, "Boy, will the boss ever be glad to hear this! And there's just time to get it scaled up and installed before the big day!"

Bob says, "Well, you better call the boss and tell him. Lord knows he's been calling us often enough the last couple or three weeks."

Joe goes over to the telephone, picks it up, and begins to dial.

The Administrator

Scientists—particularly research and development scientists—are the most difficult kind of people in the world to group into an organization and to cause to operate effectively as an organization.

This is due in part to the nature of the work they do. Research and development is a process which is marked mainly by failure— that is, many paths have to be tried before the right one is found.

It is also due to the fact that scientists are scientists. Their attitude of mind is inquiring, nonroutine, resentful and rebellious against established patterns. (This is how they find new things.) In addition, of course, is the aim of the research and development administrator to elicit from these people new ideas, new concepts, new discoveries, new applications of old theories—all of this requires a certain amount, in fact a considerable amount, of freedom on the part of the individual scientist to poke into any intellectual or developmental byway which attracts his interest or seems to him to offer promise of a solution to the problem at hand. This results, of course, in a situation in which it is very difficult to provide freedom enough for scientific inquiry and still provide enough discipline and direction to insure that the group does not ride off in all directions, dissipating its energies and wasting its resources.

In addition, of course, scientists are people. It is strange that the man of intellect is not also a reasonable man, but as someone has said, our intellect is only to serve our passions, and scientists are a very passionate people in the classic sense. They hold passionately to their beliefs; they are passionate in their pride of knowledge, in their pride of achievement, and in their pride of conviction. Scientists also have the more mundane passions, and these sometimes cause the most trouble of all. But when all of these strong passions of man are served by brilliant and competing intellects, the arguments that can result may be not only fierce but seemingly endless. A good research project occasionally founders because of disagreement as to the approach to take toward its solution. Highly intellectual individuals can marshal endless valid-sounding arguments in support of almost any position. Almost equally, arguments can be interminable over interpretation of a single set of facts, with the result that two or more scientists may disagree violently on what they have discovered. Since scientific research and development constitute a process of building brick by brick the edifice of knowledge, if you cannot agree on what brick you have discovered or how it should be placed in the wall you are constructing, it delays, obscures, or even causes failure of the structure above it.

Further, scientists have a great pride in their own professionalism —this leads them to the firm conviction that they cannot respect and therefore cannot be led by anyone who is not their intellectual peer. Obviously it is impossible for one man to be the peer of each scientist in his own specialty in a laboratory full of scientists. It is almost equally difficult to achieve enough technical eminence in a single specialty to command a degree of respect which provides a working accommodation, as the French would say, or a *modus operandi,* as the detective stories have it.

The problem of the scientific administrator is further complicated by the fact that during his formative years he has spent almost all his attention and effort on scientific pursuits (in order to achieve the necessary scientific eminence to be an administrator of scientific projects), and consequently he has not been able to devote much time or attention to the learning of management skills. If he becomes a successful manager it is usually because of innate qualities and unusual perceptiveness in dealing with people.

Why would a man want to take on such a thorny problem as that of being an administrator of a research and development laboratory? The answer, in the case of at least one of the best of them, is that he did not ask to take on the problem and he does not regard it as anything unusual now that he has it. The man is Dr. William Pickering, director of the JPL, at Pasadena, California.

Pickering's commitment to the things he believes in and the scientific pursuits he administers is so complete that he is not easily disturbed by the prickly sort of peripheral problems which would drive the average man to take up test tube or slide rule again and abandon the field of technical administration forever.

Pickering was born in New Zealand in 1910, and early exhibited an interest in a wide variety of scientific subjects, chiefly electronics (radio) and chemistry. He completed most of his schooling in New Zealand before coming to the United States in 1929. Here he matriculated at California Institute of Technology, where the faculty and administration frankly had misgivings about the immigrant from "down under." When first examination time came around, however, all these misgivings were dispelled and Pickering was revealed as an individual with already good technical training plus a remarkable potential for scientific endeavor. The next several years at Caltech were spent studying hard and getting a bachelor of science degree, doing postgraduate work, and receiving his doctorate in physics, *cum laude*.

After receiving his doctorate he taught on the Caltech campus and also conducted research work with such greats, whose influence he readily recognizes, as Dr. Robert A. Millikan. Because of these activities, Dr. Pickering early was involved in high-altitude investigations (of cosmic rays by sending instruments up in balloons) and with the problem of transmitting the information discovered by the instrumented balloons back to earth for study and analysis. This last phase, of course, is what is today called telemetry and is an important feature of our present space program in that the space probes and spacecraft that we send into orbit or to other heavenly bodies must send back by telemetry—a specialized kind of radio transmission—the information about the things that the spacecraft are encountering and discovering.

Pickering went on to establish the V-12 program in engineering, science, and management war training in the Caltech area. Subsequently, he was active in the JPL propulsion division and became technical director of the laboratory in 1954. All during this period he was in close association with such men as Dr. von Karman, John von Neumann, and other scientific giants both here and abroad. It is not, however, Pickering's experience per se which equips him for the fantastically complex job which he does so capably—it is rather the understanding and convictions which he has distilled out of these experiences. Analysis of his published and public utterances puts these in bold relief somewhat as follows:

The scientific man must be logical and at the same time flexible enough to realign his thinking and his program as the result of unexpected discoveries. Scientific research and development are usually planned in advance with some particular goal in mind, but oftentimes the most productive results come from byways not anticipated at the time the original plan was made. The scientific man must be able to "shift gears" at full throttle in order to perform more successfully as a research and development scientist.

Pickering, of course, is enthusiastic about the increasing emphasis on science in our schools and general training, but he is fully aware of the fact that men cannot be technical robots, but must be thinking individuals. He feels, however, that if a man becomes a good scientist—by virtue of the independent nature of thinking he is trained to do under the widely accepted "scientific approach"—he will become a thinking individual who can make valid decisions in walks of life other than his narrow scientific specialty.

On the subject of training, Pickering feels that all men must have some knowledge of science because science has become such a powerful force in our lives today. A man must be scientifically literate—

this does not mean he is an expert in science, but he is conversant with the scientific method and has some basic understanding of scientific terminology—to be able to appreciate this great force in our present civilization and, as a man in a free democracy, make the choices necessary to guide us in the advancement of our country and world civilization.

Pickering is very conscious of what might be called scientific diplomacy. He sees the cold war, that combat for the dominion of men's minds, much as von Clausewitz years ago saw armed conflict: simply an extension of politics. For politics in itself is an attempt to gain dominion over men's minds and influence their course of action. At the time of launching America's first satellite, Pickering was surprised at how emotionally involved the American public was in the situation; but he readily recognized the principle involved and now sees the political and geopolitical significance of all scientific activity, particularly that in his own field.

While recognizing the importance and significance of science, particularly that dealing with space exploration, Pickering is quick to caution that we must not have a blind belief that everything can be accomplished. Pickering has his feet firmly on the ground and works to convey this attitude to the general public as well as to those associated with him in the technical programs for which he is responsible. A recognition of the present limitations on what science can accomplish, particularly in space, is essential if we are to make orderly progress instead of wasting our energies and treasure on impossible schemes.

Finally, Pickering believes that it is of paramount importance that in this day and age we do explore space and make some kind of contact with other planets. This exploration, in Pickering's belief, should not be undertaken with the thought of finding new sources of wealth—though this possibility, of course, is not ruled out—but simply because it is man's destiny: this is the next step in human evolution. He further sees the growing technology of the world making this kind of activity possible and successful—perhaps after initial failures which are common to any scientific endeavor.

In all, Pickering is part mystic, part historian and prophet, certainly a philosopher, and perhaps a scientist-statesman. He loves to fly-cast for trout in the high Sierras at every opportunity; he delights in a dry martini at an appropriate moment.

In personal contact, this bristle-browed leprechaun of a man exhibits a driving force so channeled and controlled as to give a superficial impression of rigidity in his approach to things, an impression almost immediately belied by his own ready wit and appreciation for the humor of others. He seems to have the faculty, once attributed to Napoleon, of being able to switch from one line of thought to another instantaneously and completely and, in Pickering's case, with great good humor.

Here is a man suited to the times—and the times are suited to the man!

The Big Stake

Mrs. Tom Wooten, forty-four and unabashedly gray, stood before an electric skillet in which she was cooking three scrambled eggs on a frosty October morning in a heavily mortgaged suburb on the western hills of Midwest City. She was dressed in capris and a brightly colored blouse—her usual housework uniform. At the breakfast nook in one corner of the kitchen her thirteen-year-old son, Bruce, noisily ate his way through a bowl of Rice Krispies with the singlemindedness and dispatch of a bulldozer removing a picket fence. His blond crewcut head was bent low over the bowl in a natural efficiency which required the least time and shortest travel, as the spoon moved from the bowl to his mouth.

Tom Wooten, forty-six, stood thick-bodied before the bathroom mirror and inspected the results of the shave he had just given himself. Satisfied, he put on after-shave lotion, rubbed it briefly into his skin, stepped through the bathroom door to the closet in the bedroom he shared with his wife and selected a shirt. He donned the shirt and turned toward a rack of ties, where he selected one with a Paisley pattern, put it on hurriedly before the dressing table mirror, and then turned and strode firmly through the house and into the kitchen.

As Tom Wooten came through the kitchen door, his son raised his head, an errant drop of milk at the corner of his mouth, gulped down his mouthful of cereal, and said, "Hey, Pop! I saw Echo last night."

Preoccupied with thoughts of the day before him, Tom Wooten looked at his son with a mixture of love and exasperation. The quizzical, concentrating look on Tom Wooten's face was frequently an adjunct of his conversations with his son: the boy lived in a world of far-ranging and rapidly changing interests; the father, almost always deeply engrossed in details of his lumber business, often found it difficult to keep up with the kaleidoscopic shifts in his son's conversation.

Now, only half attentive to what the boy had said, Tom responded gruffly, "Whatdya mean you *saw* an echo?"

"Not *an* echo, *the* Echo. The Echo-2 satellite that we've been running those communication experiments with the Russians on."

Tom Wooten adjusted his tie at the opening of his collar and addressed himself to the problem of setting the tie clip just right. "So?"

The son grinned. "So you can't see it every night because it doesn't come by at the right time at the right altitude after sunset so that the sun's rays will strike it while it's already dark here on the surface of the earth."

"Tom," interrupted Mrs. Tom, "why don't you have some breakfast this morning?"

"Honey, how many times do I have to tell you that I don't eat breakfast any more. Too many calories!"

"Everybody ought to eat some breakfast. How about just a little coffee?"

"No!" said Tom, more loudly than he had intended.

"Hey, Pop," his son interjected, "it should be visible again tonight. Can I borrow your good camera to try and take a time exposure?"

Mrs. Wooten brought the scrambled eggs to the table, swiftly dished them onto three plates, and said to her husband, "How about just a little bite of egg, Tom? A piece of toast?"

Wooten shook his head in annoyance. His son broke in, "I'll eat 'em both!" and he reached across the breakfast nook table, picked up the plate his mother had prepared for his father, tilted it, and slid the eggs off onto his own plate with a fork. He raised his eyes to his father's. "How about the camera? Can I try it?"

"Who's going to be helping you?" asked the senior Wooten, his frown deepening. "If that left-footed character, Jim What's-his-name, is around here to stumble over it in the dark the answer is 'No.' "

"I'll do it all by myself. Can I, Pop?"

"Okay, okay," his father said impatiently, starting to turn away. "But I don't see why you're so interested in this Echo business, or in all this space stuff, for that matter!"

Mrs. Wooten came to the table with two cups of coffee and slid into her place across from her son, setting the extra cup of coffee on the side nearest her husband. She looked up at him. "Just a cup of coffee?"

"Why do you bug me?" the husband said. "I don't want breakfast, and it's the easiest meal for me to cut out."

She responded a little plaintively, "I just think everybody ought to eat breakfast. You could cut down on lunches . . ."

Tom Wooten snorted and addressed himself again to his son. "You can use the camera all right, but be careful!" He repeated, "Careful! That thing cost over four hundred bucks and I don't want to come home and find it all in pieces. I can't see where this space business is so important, but . . ." His voice trailed away.

His son looked up with a speculative look in his eyes and said, "I'd think *you*'d be interested in it too."

His father seemed mildly surprised. "Why me? What's that got to do with the lumber business?"

"Well, not directly maybe, but some of your customers work on space stuff, don't they? And you pay taxes too!" he finished in a rush.

The father moved closer to the table. "Where did you get all this?"

The boy seemed mildly embarrassed now that he had caught his father's full attention. He shrugged and went on. "In science yesterday Mr. Hobert was telling us we could see the Echo last night and the kids got to asking questions and he told us quite a bit about the space program. Gee, it costs a lot, too, doesn't it?"

"Yes," his father said slowly, "it sure does! And you're right, I pay taxes. Plenty!"

The son raised his head again, his face brightening with a new thought. "But gee, Pop, it's neat! This is the biggest adventure since Columbus—maybe bigger! Exploring space and all that stuff." He subsided now, overawed by his own enthusiasm. "How many millions make a billion, Pop?"

"A thousand," his father answered absently. He took a deep breath and straightened up. "Yes, it's a lot of money us taxpayers are putting in this." He turned directly to his son. "It *is* important and I *am* interested. The business keeps me so occupied I don't think about it very often, but you young ones should. You're growing up in the space age!"

The boy brightened again. "Yeah, that's what Mr. Hobert said, too. He said we all have a big stake in the space thing—you guys who pay the taxes and us kids who'll be around to see all the changes on earth that come from space exploration. What does that mean, Pop?"

"I guess nobody knows exactly what it means, son, because these things haven't happened yet." His voice turned slightly grim. "And don't think us old folks are the only taxpayers. You youngsters are going to get to pay them, too, in your turn!"

His son became eager at this prospective participation. "But it's worth it, isn't it, Pop?"

His father reached over and ruffled his crew cut. "Yes, I guess it's worth it. It's a big stake, but it's a big game." He turned and started out of the room.

His wife got quickly to her feet and followed him as he went to the hall closet and shrugged into his coat. He gave her a parting kiss and went through the door, smiling back at her.

"Have a good day!" she called and closed the door after him.

9. Where Are We Going?

To Other Planets and Stars

Most prosaically, perhaps, we are going to the moon, the planets, and possibly some of the nearer stars. It is quite possible that man himself will land upon the moon and some of the more hospitable planets. For the more distant planets, even those such as Jupiter and Saturn, which are respectively 483 million miles and 886 million miles from the sun—and certainly for Pluto at 4,600 million miles from the sun—we will probably have to rely for the foreseeable future upon instrumented spacecraft without men aboard. The nearby stars, if visited in this century, will certainly be visited only by instrumented spacecraft, though these will be of a sophistication not now dreamed of. Matching this sophistication in spacecraft we will have to improve our techniques in communication still further, so that data can be telemetered back across several light years of space in a form and such a static-free condition that the information can be received intelligibly and interpreted on earth. The information will certainly be in a form, among others, which corresponds to present-day television transmission so that we can get a closeup look at the distant planets in the solar system and perhaps the planets in any system around the nearest stars.

These spacecraft probings of the solar system, manned landings on the moon and perhaps Mars, the televised flybys of distant

The moon, our first target. (*Mount Wilson and Palomar Observatories*)

planets, and the similarly televised exploration of the planetary system of some other star will be the physical manifestations of an even deeper intellectual probing of the universe in which we live.

These spacecraft trips that we have just described will be like the planes which carry men from New York to Los Angeles. The really important thing, however, is the reasons why men travel from New York to Los Angeles, and the intellectual or emotional experiences that they have during the trip.

In sending a spacecraft into some deep reach of space, the important thing will be what man and the instruments helping him are able to determine about the nature of their trip and the nature of the universe in which the trip is made.

To a Better Understanding

One of the most profoundly interesting results expected to come from all this space traveling will be to verify or disprove some of the theories about the universe itself.

When man first started thinking about his universe he assumed that a flat, table-like earth was its center. The earth was so flat and the table it formed so limited, that early men were afraid to explore the oceans very far beyond the shore for fear they would "fall off" the edge of the earth. In this view, the sun, the moon, all the planets, and the stars revolved about the earth. This theory was first put forth by Ptolemy, a famous astronomer and mathematician who lived from about 100 to 170 A.D. The belief was largely held throughout Europe for nearly fourteen hundred years until the Polish astronomer, Copernicus, finally proved it wrong. Both Copernicus and his follower, Galileo, were persecuted for their belief and their writings on the subject were banned by the Church for almost two hundred years after the discovery was first made.

Einstein is generally credited with the theory of the expanding universe, which holds that all galaxies are traveling away from us at fantastic speeds, like the fragments of an exploding bomb. In this theory, the most distant galaxies seem to be moving the most rapidly away from our solar system, and consequently this theory seems like only a slightly more sophisticated version of the one in which the earth is the center of the universe.

The basis for this theory is that light from distant galaxies shows what is called a "red shift." The red shift is the old Doppler theory applied to bodies moving at speeds which are appreciable fractions of the speed of light.

Many astronomers, however, do not believe the idea of the expanding universe is the proper explanation for this phenomenon. They prefer to believe that light may undergo some "decay" effect in its travel through the universe. If this is true—even though not yet understood—it would simply mean that light as it travels through space gets "tired," and the farther it travels the more tired it gets. This tiredness would result in slowing the frequency of the light vibrations and therefore would make the light appear to move toward the low-frequency or red end of the spectrum.

Magnetic fields affect the transmission of light. The early, faltering steps we have already made into space indicate that apparently all space is inhabited by weak magnetic fields. These fields are weak only by comparison to small, intense, local magnetic fields that we can measure on the earth. The magnetic fields of space occupy such tremendous areas of space—in fact, they appear to be all-pervading —that even though they are weak by comparison to local magnetic fields on earth their total effect on light passing through the limitless reaches of space may indeed account for the red shift.

Another matter of considerable present interest is an attempt to determine the sources of the tremendous radio energy that reaches us from some locations in outer space. Again, the scientists cannot agree. The most commonly held belief at the moment is that these sources of tremendous radio energy must be the result of colliding or exploding galaxies, producing energies beyond anything we can even imagine. But an alternate explanation may again have to do with the tremendous magnetic fields of space which can shape and "channel" the energies of the charged particles which make up the plasma that occupies all space. In this type of situation, the vast magnetic fields of inner-galactic space could act like lenses, in much the same way that the electron "gun" in your television set concentrates the stream of electrons into a spot that makes a picture on your television tube.

Some of the sources of extremely great radio energy may not be true *sources,* but—concentrated by the lens effect of interstellar magnetic fields—may instead be concentrations or accumulations of energy which are detected by our radio telescopes.

There are many other fascinating questions about the universe which will undoubtedly be answered by our space probes; many of them will be questions that we do not even know now to ask. But coming closer to home, it seems certain that space exploration will give us much more information on the origin of our world, of life, and of man himself.

It is interesting to note that the story of the creation of the earth in the Bible is roughly paralleled by what scientists believe they have learned about the creation of the earth from studying the earth and the universe in which it exists.

The book of Genesis starts:

In the beginning God created the heaven and the earth.
And the earth was without form, and void; and darkness was upon the face of the deep. And the spirit of God moved upon the face of the waters.
And God said, Let there be light: and there was light.
And God saw the light, that it was good: and God divided the light from the darkness.
And God called the light Day, and the darkness he called Night. And the evening and the morning were the first day.

If now we can assume, as seems highly probable, that the original version of the Bible was written by early Hebraic peoples who often spoke in symbolism rather than in the literal language of today, it is easy to realize that the "first day" could mean the first phase or period of creation.

If this assumption is made, the statements quoted above very closely parallel the beliefs of many scientists about the creation of the earth. For in the beginning, these people believe, the earth *was* without form and was probably a gaseous collection of matter trailing and eventually revolving about the sun in approximately the orbit the earth now occupies. In time, this gaseous material coalesced into the planet that we know, but even in those days the early planet was continuously covered by clouds (as the newly formed earth began cooling), and it perhaps rained continuously, thus filling up the seas as the rocks cooled.

Again back to the Bible, Genesis 1:6, 8 says: "And God said, Let there be a firmament in the midst of the waters, and let it divide the waters from the waters. . . . And the evening and the morning were the second day."

The scientists again find, through the study of the earth itself, a close parallel to this statement. The cooling earth, which was first completely covered with water, acquired, as it cooled further, some "wrinkles" in its cooling and shrinking surface which thrust up mountains and continents above the surface of the all-covering waters. This development occurred in what the scientists call the Archeozoic era, in which the Laurentian revolution saw rocks rumple into mountains in Canada, and molten rock harden under the surface to form great masses of granite on which the continents formed. All this happened about 2 billion, 100 million years ago.

Going back to the Bible again, Genesis 1:11, 13: "And God said, Let the earth bring forth grass, the herb yielding seed, and the fruit tree yielding fruit after his kind, whose seed is in itself, upon the earth: and it was so. . . . And the evening and the morning were the third day."

Scientists place this development about 1 billion, 300 million to 1 billion years ago, during which limy sea plants became the first living things of which we find any geologic record. Later, other marine plants developed. This occurred in the late Archeozoic era and the Proterozoic era. Later, in the Paleozoic era, land plants appeared about 350 million years ago, and subsequently these evolved into the trees, ferns, and vines which were the early ancestors of the kinds of flora that exist today.

From what we know now it is difficult to draw a close parallel with the fourth day described in Genesis, but if we want to stretch our imagination a little bit it would be possible to speculate that this was the period in which the earth and the solar system assumed their present place in the universe.

On the fifth day, the Bible says that God created "every living creature," except man.

The scientific parallel to this started in the late Paleozoic era, about 220 million years ago, and lasted through what we call the Mesozoic era and part of the Cenozoic era, up to about 13 million years ago. By this time the patterns of all animal life, except that of man, were fairly well established.

On the sixth day, the Bible says: ". . . God created man in his own image . . ." Scientists put the beginning of this development at approximately 2 million years ago. Contemporary observers, conscious as we all are of how far short of the divine image man still falls, must believe that we are perhaps living in the sixth day of creation right now!

Be all this speculation as it may, in space exploration we will at least find out more about the origin of life and possibly the origin of man as we are able to examine other planets in more advanced or perhaps less advanced stages of development than earth.

To Rich Technological Rewards

We are also going to realize tremendous technical advantages from our efforts to put spacecraft and men into space. Throughout recorded history, every major war has brought significant technical advances which, as soon as the war was over, were utilized in peacetime pursuits. The old philosophy of "beating swords into plowshares" has brought great technical advances.

One of the reasons that technical advances follow wars is that the crisis of war has always made man work harder and invent more ingeniously in the name of self-preservation. Any other motivation which would have driven man to put forth great effort and do serious thinking about his problems, would perhaps have the same result.

In the present situation, the technical advances are bound to be infinitely greater than they would be as a result of war. There are several reasons for this. First, is the dazzling fact that because of our present stage of technological development half of all the scientists and engineers who have ever lived in the world are alive and working at their profession today. This rather startling statement merely reflects the fact that we are putting infinitely more effort into research and development now than ever before.

Second, in a war situation it is inevitable that much human effort goes into devising and creating weapons of destruction. This means that the technical advantages which carry over into the later peacetime society are by-products of the war effort and represent, usually, a relatively small percentage of this effort. In the present situation, however, the emphasis is on types of technology which are useful and directly applicable to peacetime society, with a smaller percentage going into the creation of weapons of destruction. Thus, out of this much greater technical effort we will realize a much larger percentage of useful developments.

Third, the scientific and technical community is making a much more comprehensive effort to save, and to make generally available, the results of their scientific discoveries.

It is not often recognized that it was only toward the end of World War II that Dr. Vannevar Bush (whatever his shortcomings may have been as a prophet of the missile and space age) had the foresight to realize that the end of the war would interrupt many scientific and technical developments in mid-career and that if something was not done to record the developments up to that time, much technical knowledge would be lost to the United States (and to the world) until it was rediscovered. With this thought in mind, Dr. Bush established what was then known as the Summary Technical

Report Series. The closing months of the war and the year or two immediately following V-J Day were devoted in many laboratories and research organizations throughout the country to making final records of the war-initiated programs on which so much effort had been spent and which were brought to a halt at the close of the war.

Stemming from this idea of Dr. Bush's has grown the whole concept of careful documentation of technical work and the rapid interchange of information regarding new discoveries throughout the scientific community. Thus it is that our present technology is marked less by great geniuses than it is by the successful harnessing and intelligent direction of the many small technical contributions made by ordinary scientists and engineers. Each one contributes knowledge of a specific advance he has been able to make and receives, in turn, knowledge of developments others have accomplished. In this way our scientific edifice is erected brick by brick as though it were a masonry wall—each man contributing a brick in his turn and climbing up on the wall erected by others to place the next brick. In this way the entire technical effort advances much more rapidly than would in any other way be possible.

To the Better Competition

Still another thing which we *may* achieve through our space effort is avoidance of war. There is, of course, no guarantee that this will be the outcome of the race in space, but it seems at least a possibility. Man is a combative and competitive animal who seems to perform best and realize his highest capabilities under the driving pressures of competition.

In the past, war has been the great competition—it has made heroes out of individuals and even out of whole nations. War has led to advances in engineering which have benefited succeeding generations. War has led to the development of techniques for supplying armies, cities, and other large masses of population which have brought better food to more tables and better health to millions.

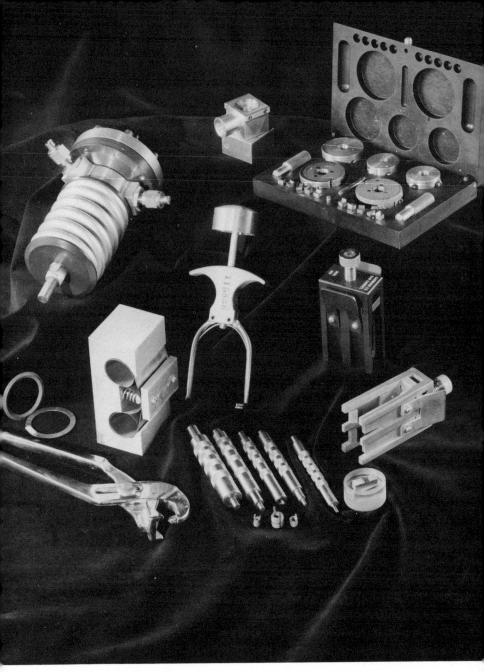

Technological advances: from Syncom to workaday tools saving time and money and increasing productivity. (*Left* (syncom): *NASA photo; right* (tools): *Jet Propulsion Laboratory*)

War has inspired individuals and groups to heights of effort and nobility of beliefs which they had never dreamed of in the intervening doldrums of peace.

In addition, man needs drama, adventure, and excitement if he is not to stagnate—in short, man needs to be disciplined by struggle.

Certainly the race for space and, perhaps eventually, the cooperation of all earth peoples in the great struggle to conquer the unknowns of space is a better competition than war. It may prove as satisfying to man's emotional needs, and so filled with adventure and excitement that he will turn from killing his fellow man to trying to destroy the barriers of ignorance which limit his knowledge of himself and his universe.

In any event, and wherever else we may be going in space, we will be piercing the unknown. This seems to be man's mission on earth—and off it!

Index

About the Author

A. EDWARD TYLER was born in Omaha, Nebraska, and attended high school there. His father, Dr. A. F. Tyler, was one of the pioneers in the use of X ray and radium in the treatment of cancer, and he wanted his son to be a doctor also. But young Edward had other ideas and compromised with his father by majoring in chemistry at Grinnell College, Iowa. After working for some years in a family printing and publishing business he then helped build LCT and LCM landing craft on the banks of the Missouri River during the war. A bone infection had kept him out of the army.

After the war Mr. Tyler moved to California where he worked for the U. S. Navy Electronics Laboratory, the U. S. Naval Ordnance Test Station, and various government contractors. For some years he was with the Jet Propulsion Laboratory of the California Institute of Technology, a prime mover in space activities which is operated by the National Aeronautics and Space Administration, working with their reports group and then with information systems. He now does consulting work in the field of computer-based information systems and operates a technical translation service.

Working closely with the space program himself, he has been able to talk to various people engaged in it and observe them at their work. Much of the book is thus his own distillation of the information available to him in his day-to-day work.

Some of his hobbies are photography, bridge, swimming, sailing small boats, deep sea fishing (great when the fish are biting!), and writing. He is a member of the Greater Los Angeles Press Club, the Society of Technical Writers and Publishers, the California Institute of Technology Management Club, and other organizations. He is married and has five children.

Format by Sidney Feinberg
Set in Linotype Times Roman
Composed by Brown Bros. Linotypers, Inc.
Printed by Murray Printing Co.
Bound by Haddon Craftsmen, Inc.
HARPER & ROW, PUBLISHERS, INCORPORATED